Essential Maths 7H

Homework Book

Elmwood Press

First published 2008 by
Elmwood Press
80 Attimore Road
Welwyn Garden City
Herts. AL8 6LP
Tel. 01707 333232

Reprinted 2012, 2013

ISBN 9781 906 622 008

Typeset and illustrated by Domex e-Data Pvt. Ltd.
Printed and bound by Bookwell

CONTENTS

UNIT 1

1.1 Whole number arithmetic

HWK 1M — **Main Book page 1**

1 Copy and fill in the empty boxes

   a $3 \times \boxed{} + 6 = 306$ **b** $5 \times \boxed{} + 3 = 5003$ **c** $4 \times \boxed{} + \boxed{} = 49$

   d $6 \times \boxed{} + 5 = 65$ **e** $2 \times \boxed{} + \boxed{} = 208$ **f** $9 \times \boxed{} + 4 \times \boxed{} = 9040$

2 Write these numbers in words.

   a 4315   **b** 70000   **c** 32140   **d** 6842300

3 Show how you can use the numbers 72, 4000, 200 and 6 to make the number 3866 by adding and subtracting.

4 **a** How many three figure numbers can be formed by using the figures 2, 3 and 7 once each?

   b Write down the largest *even* number from your three figure numbers in part (a).

   c Find the sum of all your three figure numbers in part (a).

   d Find the difference between the two lowest *odd* three figure numbers in part (a).

5 Copy and complete

   a $482186 + \boxed{} = 492186$ **b** $73296 - \boxed{} = 72296$

6 Colin wins £8104653 on the National Lottery. Write this number in words.

7 Find four numbers $\boxed{a}$, $\boxed{b}$, $\boxed{c}$ and $\boxed{d}$ for which

   $6 \times \boxed{a} + 3 \times \boxed{b} + 4 \times \boxed{c} + 9 \times \boxed{d} = 63049$

HWK 2M — **Main Book page 3**

Work out

1 $718 - 493$ **2** $4180 - 745$ **3** $132 + 168 - 175$

4 Add each pair of numbers and write each answer in the box below.

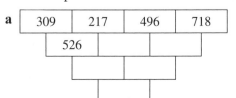

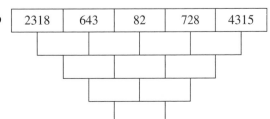

5 Copy and complete these multiplication squares.

a

×			6		
			36		
		18			
		42			
			45	10	
	72	27			

b

×					
			36	45	
		21		15	
		56			64
	24				
	42	49			

6 Work out

    a 48×7 **b** 516×8 **c** 187×6

7 Carly has 1200 newsletters to deliver. When she returns home she has 304 newsletters left. How many newsletters has she actually delivered?

HWK 2E ———————————————————————————— **Main Book page 4**

Copy and complete the cross number puzzle.

1		2		3	4
				5	
6			7		
		8			9
10	11		12		
13					

Clues across

  1. $139 + 324 - 217$

  3. $3 \times 3 \times 3$

  5. $123 - 64$

  6. $32654 + 21897 + 30185$

  8. $71 - 42$

10. A quarter of 272

12. $56 \times 9 + 130$

13. $2653 + 4186 - 1099$

Clues down

  1. 38×6

  2. $8520 - 2148$

  3. $4 \times 4 \times 4 \times 4$

  4. Half of 158

  7. $(539 \times 7) + 187$

  9. 27×9

10. $418 - 353$

11. $3218 - 3131$

3

1 A man does not eat for one week. How many hours is that?

2 How many 1p coins are in £2700?

3 What belongs in each empty box?

   a 671 − ☐ = 485   **b** ☐ × 8 = 184   **c** ☐ − 350 = 479

   d 3000 ÷ ☐ = 60   **e** 638 + ☐ = 1226   **f** ☐ ÷ 6 = 32

4 I am a two digit number. The difference between my digits is 1. The product of my digits is 20. Which two numbers might I be?

5 Charlie exercises for 150 minutes each time he does a session. How many hours of exercise has he done when he has completed 30 sessions?

6 The numbers 5, 7 and 8 can make 43 because 8 + 5 × 7 = 43.

   Fill in the boxes with either +, −, × or ÷ below.

   a 3 ☐ 8 ☐ 6 = 51   **b** 5 ☐ 2 ☐ 9 = 1

   c 4 ☐ 6 ☐ 5 ☐ 8 = 21   **d** 9 ☐ 3 ☐ 4 ☐ 7 = 0

7 2008 was a leap year. How many hours were there in February?

8 If 234 × 103 = 24102, work out 236 × 103 without multiplying.

9 Cans of coke at 53p each are put in packs of 10. Ten packs are put in a box. One hundred boxes are put in a container. Find the cost of 100 containers.

10 Find three numbers which multiply together to give 288 and which add up to 21.

   ☐ × ☐ × ☐ = 288   ☐ + ☐ + ☐ = 21

Find the outputs from these number machines.

1 6 → ×0 → ◢

2 12 → ×3 → ÷9 → ◤

3 9 → ×7 → +18 → ☺

4 15 → +36 → ÷3 → ■

5 13 → +43 → ÷21 → ?

6 7 → ×8 → −24 → ⊂⊲

7 36 → ÷3 → +64 → ★

8 19 → +47 → ×0 → $

9 8 → ×11 → ÷4 → ⊂⊲

10 54 → −39 → ÷5 → ?

4

11 3 → ×8 → −15 → ×6 → +46 → ■

12 20 → ×10 → −113 → +3 → ÷30 → ×9 → $

13 60 → ÷4 → +17 → ×5 → ×2 → ÷10 → ☺

14 18 → ×2 → +9 → ÷5 → ×40 → +40 → ÷50 → ↑

15 25 → +19 → −13 → ×0 → ×6 → +29 → ×3 → +13 → ◢

HWK 4E ──────────────────────────────── **Main Book page 6**

Find the inputs to these number machines.

1 ★ → ×7 → 21

2 ◢ → ÷3 → 13

3 ■ → +21 → −13 → 16

4 ↑ → +13 → ×4 → 80

5 ☺ → +6 → ×7 → 77

6 ? → +41 → ÷8 → 7

7 ◣ → −3 → ×9 → 72

8 ● → −5 → ×12 → 36

9 ⋈ → ×2 → ÷8 → 5

10 $ → ÷4 → ÷3 → 7

11 ▬ → +70 → ÷4 → 20

12 ☺ → ÷8 → ×30 → 60

13 ? → ×35 → −40 → 65

14 ● → ÷5 → ×15 → 75

15 ↑ → ÷20 → +39 → 44

16 ⋈ → ÷3 → ×8 → 200

17 ▬ → ×8 → +68 → 100

18 ▼ → −109 → +32 → 223

19 ◢ → ×9 → −57 → 24

20 $ → +63 → ÷2 → 39

HWK 5M ──────────────────────────────── **Main Book page 7**

What operation is taking place in each of these machines?

1 15 → ? → 12
   14 → ? → 11
   13 → ? → 10

2 7 → ? → 42
   4 → ? → 24
   9 → ? → 54

3 28 → ? → 14
   12 → ? → 6
   32 → ? → 16

For questions **4** to **9** copy and complete the number machines after working out the operation for each.

4
15 → [ ] → 8
9 → [ ] → 2
21 → [ ] → ?
19 → [ ] → ?
? → [ ] → 10

5
3 → [ ] → 24
9 → [ ] → ?
7 → [ ] → 56
? → [ ] → 40
20 → [ ] → ?

6
14 → [ ] → 27
6 → [ ] → ?
? → [ ] → 44
? → [ ] → 18
18 → [ ] → 31

7
8 → [ ] → 72
2 → [ ] → ?
7 → [ ] → 63
? → [ ] → 81
? → [ ] → 36

8
30 → [ ] → 11
23 → [ ] → ?
54 → [ ] → ?
41 → [ ] → 22
? → [ ] → 19

9
32 → [ ] → 8
20 → [ ] → 5
44 → [ ] → ?
? → [ ] → 20
? → [ ] → 7

HWK 5E ———————————————————— **Main Book page 8**

1 Find the two operations which give *both* the results shown.

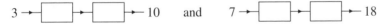

3 → [ ] → [ ] → 10   and   7 → [ ] → [ ] → 18

2 Find the two operations which give *both* the results shown.

6 → [ ] → [ ] → 13   and   9 → [ ] → [ ] → 22

3 Find the two operations which give *all* three results shown below.

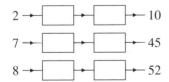

2 → [ ] → [ ] → 10

7 → [ ] → [ ] → 45

8 → [ ] → [ ] → 52

4 For each chart find the *single* operation which performs the same operation as those shown.

a In → [× 10] → [÷ 5] → [× 2] → Out   **b** In → [+ 20] → [− 8] → [+ 9] → [− 6] → Out

c In → [+ 3] → [× 2] → [− 6] → Out   **d** In → [+ 89] → [− 17] → [− 14] → [− 10] → Out

6

5 Find the input number which gives the same output number for *both* charts below.

In → ×5 → −4 → Out   In → ×3 → +2 → Out

6 Find the input number which gives the same output number for *both* charts below.

In → ×2 → +3 → Out   In → ×4 → −7 → Out

1 Copy and complete.

a $49 ÷ \square = 7$ **b** $36 ÷ \square = 12$ **c** $\square ÷ 4 = 7$

d $\square ÷ 9 = 2$ **e** $400 ÷ \square = 40$ **f** $\square ÷ 5 = 20$

g $\square ÷ 8 = 9$ **h** $63 ÷ \square = 9$ **i** $\square ÷ 6 = 8$

j $300 ÷ \square = 5$ **k** $90 ÷ \square = 9$ **l** $\square ÷ 10 = 11$

2 Copy and complete these number chains.

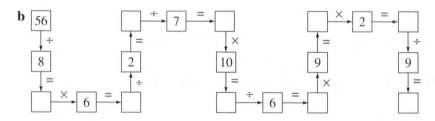

3 Copy and complete:

a $(6 + \square) ÷ 3 = 5$ **b** $(23 + \square) ÷ 8 = 6$ **c** $(67 − \square) ÷ 5 = 7$

d $(81 − \square) ÷ 7 = 8$ **e** $(27 + \square) ÷ 8 = 10$ **f** $(116 − \square) ÷ 6 = 9$

4 What number, when multiplied by 9 and then divided by 3, gives an answer of 6?

5 What number, when divided by 8 and then multiplied by 7, gives 56?

6 What number, when divided by 6 and then multiplied by 11, gives 99?

1 Copy and complete the multiplication squares. The number outside the square are always 2, 3, 4, 5, 6, 7, 8, 9.

a

	4	3	8	
9		27		
6				30
			16	
7				

b

	7	2		
			12	
4	12			20
				40
		63		

c

		6		
			15	
		48		
8		12	36	

d

		18	10	
		36		
			40	24
			30	

2 In the next three squares you may have the same number at the top and along the side of the square.

a

	3			
		36	20	
	18			12
24				6
	27	81		
			35	

b

			20		28
				48	
			35		
6	27			21	
			40		

c

42	24			
49				56
		27		
			25	
		9		

Work out

1 4)128 **2** 3)159 **3** 5)135 **4** 7)168

5 3)201 **6** 6)276 **7** 8)552 **8** 9)657

9 7)609 **10** 8)392 **11** 4)2732 **12** 9)5148

13 480 ÷ 5 **14** 432 ÷ 8 **15** 574 ÷ 7 **16** 2636 ÷ 4

17 4466 ÷ 7 **18** 4113 ÷ 9 **19** 3928 ÷ 8 **20** 5565 ÷ 7

21 Which is larger and by how much?

 6) 2172   or   8) 2936

22 £4578 is shared equally between 6 people. How much money does each person get?

23 A teacher divides 153 pencils equally between 9 children. How many pencils does each child get?

24 Is 2569 ÷ 7 larger than 352? If so, by how much?

25 A factory makes 4110 toys to sell for Christmas. The toys are delivered to shops in six equal lorry loads. How many toys go in each lorry?

26 Work out

    a 26388 ÷ 4   **b** 713008 ÷ 8   **c** 2497943 ÷ 7

HWK 8M ──────────────────────────────── **Main Book page 12**

Write each answer with a remainder.

1 5)198   **2** 7)615   **3** 8)316   **4** 6)496

5 519 ÷ 9   **6** 3014 ÷ 6   **7** 5167 ÷ 3   **8** 9241 ÷ 8

9 Which division gives the larger remainder and by how much?

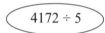

    4172 ÷ 5   or   2817 ÷ 7

10 5128 ÷ 9   **11** 7293 ÷ 6   **12** 83197 ÷ 8   **13** 56324 ÷ 10

14 7)3140   **15** 4)58375   **16** 6)597183   **17** 6)283174

HWK 8E ──────────────────────────────── **Main Book page 12**

In these questions, think carefully about whether you should round *up* or *down*.

1 30 children want to play football. How many full teams of 7 players can be made?

2 A taxi can carry 5 people. How many taxis are needed to carry 32 people?

3 A cinema ticket costs £6. How many tickets can be bought for £50?

4 An egg box holds 6 eggs. How many boxes do you need for 304 eggs?

5 How many 7 pence chews can I buy with £2?

6 9 children can sleep in a large tent. How many tents are needed for 110 children?

7   **a** How many Thunderbird 1 models can I buy with £150?

       b How many Thunderbird 2 models can I buy with £212?

Models	
£8	Thunderbird 1
£7	Thunderbird 2
£4	Thunderbird 4

8   Pencils are packed into boxes of 8. How many boxes are filled completely if you have 573 pencils?

9   How many 6 cm pieces of wood can be cut from a 2 metre piece of wood?

10   A charity puts £3 into each Christmas gift box. How many gift boxes can be done in this way if the charity has £6500?

11   Find the missing numbers below (each box contains a single digit).

   a   4   9   r   4   **b**   8   8   7   r   1   **c**   6   4   3   r   6

       9⟌ 4 4 ☐   6⟌ 5 3 2 ☐   ☐⟌ 5 ☐ ☐ ☐

1.2 Long Multiplication and division

HWK 1M ────────────────────────────── **Main Book page 14**

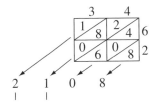

Use the grid method or any other way you wish to use to work out the questions below.

1   26 × 32   **2**   35 × 26   **3**   53 × 46   **4**   62 × 37

5   28 × 67   **6**   43 × 84   **7**   47 × 78   **8**   94 × 53

9   **a** Danny is a decorator. He buys 24 pots of blue paint and 29 pots of yellow paint. How much does this cost in total?

       b 'SPLASH' painters buy 38 pots of blue, 23 pots of pink, 49 pots of yellow and 34 pots of red. How much do they spend in total?

Paint cost per pot		
5*l*	pink	£12
5*l*	blue	£13
10*l*	red	£21
10*l*	yellow	£23

10

Use any method to work out the questions below.

1 317×26
2 227×43
3 54×526
4 46×718

5 74×436
6 825×64
7 237×182
8 649×328

9 In a school assembly there are 12 rows of chairs. Each row has 23 chairs. How many chairs are there in total?

10 Carla earns £23 per hour. One month she works for 152 hours. Ben earns £21 per hour. During the month he works 5 days each week for 4 weeks. On each day he works for 8 hours. Who earns the most money during this month and by how much?

11 How many hours are there in a leap year?

12 Without using a calculator, estimate how many heart beats a man has had if he is 80 years old (assume his heart beats 80 times each minute).

Work out these questions. There are no remainders.

1 $6\overline{)882}$
2 $14\overline{)588}$
3 $13\overline{)689}$
4 $23\overline{)575}$

5 $672 \div 42$
6 $1377 \div 27$
7 $1404 \div 39$
8 $2772 \div 44$

9 $629 \div 37$
10 $1216 \div 19$
11 $1728 \div 48$
12 $2492 \div 28$

Work out these questions. There may be remainders.

1 $285 \div 16$
2 $416 \div 28$
3 $739 \div 19$
4 $624 \div 36$

5 Each box of matches contains 43 matches. How many boxes can be filled from 750 matches?

6 There are 28 children in a class. The teacher has 402 sweets and wants to give each child the same number of sweets. What is the greatest number of sweets a child gets and how many sweets are left over?

7 A bus can carry 57 people. How many buses are needed to carry 765 people?

8 Copy and complete

a $\square \times 34 = 1224$
b $1431 \div 53 = \square$
c $47 \times \square = 3149$

9 A school needs 450 rulers. They are sold in packs of 24. How many packs will the school need to order? How many extra rulers will there be?

10 How many 34p stamps can be bought with £5 and how much money will be left over?

11 Copy and complete this multiplication square.

	13	?	?
?	299	?	736
?	338	?	?
19	?	665	?

1.3 Decimals

HWK 1M	**Main Book page 19**

1 Write the answers only

   a 0.3 + 0.5   **b** 1.8 + 0.4   **c** 1.5 − 0.6   **d** 3.4 − 0.8

   e 3.7 − 0.9   **f** 1 + 0.6   **g** 0.9 + 0.7 + 0.8   **h** 2.2 − 0.3

2 Two chefs use 2.7 kg of flour and 1.8 kg of flour. They had 5 kg of flour to start with.

   a How much flour do they use in total?

   b How much flour do they have left?

3 What does the digit 4 in 8.427 represent? And the 2? And the 7?

4 Write down nine hundredths as a decimal number.

5 Write down seventeen hundredths as a decimal number.

6 Terry weighs 44.535 kg. Two weeks later he weighs 44.235 kg. How much weight has he lost?

7 Which is the larger of each pair of numbers below?

   a 0.6 or 0.62   **b** 0.523 or 0.533   **c** 0.28 or 0.82   **d** 0.9 or 0.009

   e 5.7 or 5.07   **f** 0.8 or 0.75   **g** 0.09 or $\frac{7}{10}$ **h** 4 or 4.00

   i 3.04 or 3.3   **j** $\frac{8}{100}$ or 0.7

8 Find the missing number in each question below.

   a 7.53 + ? = 7.73   **b** 0.816 − ? = 0.616   **c** ? + 5.143 = 5.149   **d** 12.327 − ? = 12.027

9 Write down eighteen thousandths as a decimal number.

10 Write down three thousandths as a decimal number.

HWK 2M ——————————————————————————————— **Main Book page 20**

1 Write the numbers in order of size, smallest first.

a 0.48, 0.28, 0.33   b 0.19, 0.34, 0.2   c 0.12, 0.03, 0.1

d 0.92, 0.925, 0.903   e 0.68, 0.73, 0.7, 0.62   f 9.399, 9.31, 9.2, 9.36

g 0.307, 0.4, 0.08, 0.24   h 0.4, 0.53, 0.52, 0.501

2 a Increase 9.32 by $\dfrac{1}{10}$ b Decrease 10.03 by $\dfrac{1}{10}$

3 a Increase 7.287 by $\dfrac{1}{1000}$ b Decrease 16.527 by $\dfrac{1}{100}$

4 Six sprinters in a 200 m race ran the following times (in seconds):

| Matt 26.3 | Carl 26.24 | Dan 26.27 | Sunil 26.41 | Tom 26.19 | Alex 26.4 |

a Who won the race?

b Write down the names in the order that they finished.

5 Write these numbers in order of size, smallest first.   0.039

0.040 $\dfrac{3}{10}$,   0.309,   0.032, $\dfrac{3}{100}$,   0.4, $\dfrac{39}{100}$

0.300   0.030   0.390

HWK 2E ——————————————————————————————— **Main Book page 22**

Work out the value indicated by the arrow.

1

2

3

4

5

6

7

8

9

10

11

12

13

14

15

16

17

18

HWK 3M — **Main Book page 22**

Work out

1 8.72
  + 4.91

2 17
  + 3.6

3 16.4
  −13.6

4 6
  − 4.3

5 13 + 0.47

6 3.6 + 6.19

7 3.2 − 1.9

8 9 − 6.8

9 0.3 + 5 + 2.14

10 17.6 + 3.82 + 4

11 16.4 − 11.7

12 5.4 − 2.16

13 19 − 5.82

14 7.216 + 5 + 3.8

15 13 − 4.28

16 4.38 + 0.179 + 7

17 Find the number which belongs in each empty box.

a 1.8 + ☐ = 3.25

b ☐ + 1.87 = 12

c 2.9 − ☐ = 1.17

d ☐ − 0.58 = 7.6

18 Find the missing digits

a 3 . ☐ 6
  + ☐ . 9 ☐
  ‾‾‾‾‾‾‾
  6 . 1 9

b ☐ . 7 3 ☐
  + 4 . 1 ☐ 4
  ‾‾‾‾‾‾‾‾‾
  9 . ☐ 1 2

c 6 . ☐ 2
  − 4 . 1 ☐
  ‾‾‾‾‾‾‾
  ☐ . 6 5

HWK 3E — **Main Book page 23**

1 What must be added to £4.39 to make £5?

2 What must be added to £12.37 to make £19?

3 Didier bought a burger for £2.33, a drink for 78 p and an ice cream for £1.10. How much change will he have from a £10 note?

4 Jasmine bought a shirt for £21.89 and some trousers for £29.50. Alonso spent £33.45 on a sweatshirt and £18.10 on swimming trunks. Who spent the most and by how much?

5

ROUGE CAFE			
tea	95 p	chips	90 p
coffee	£1.10	sandwich	£1.87
coke	85 p	pizza	£4.19
lemonade	70 p	fish	£2.75
orange juice	£1.15	burger	£1.65

Cassie and Shane go to the Rouge Cafe.

a Cassie wants to buy a pizza and coke. She has £5. Does she have enough money?

b Shane has £10. He lends Cassie the extra money she needs and also buys an orange juice. How much money does Shane have left?

14

6 Find the number which belongs in each empty box.

   a ☐ + 0.072 = 0.115   **b** ☐ − 0.006 = 5.735   **c** ☐ − 0.049 = 9.689

   d 14.624 − ☐ = 0.378

7

	0.74	5.6	
		4.64	
	3.15		5.85
3.18			
5.83	7.1		

Copy and complete this addition square.

8 I can walk to a shop and buy a radio for £27.85 and some headphones for £8.99. In a second shop I can buy the radio for £25.99 and the headphones for £6.75. How much do I save by going to the second shop if the return bus fare is £2.15?

9 Find the value of ? below:

   ? × 10 − 7.18 = 28.82

HWK 4M   **Main Book page 25**

1 Copy and complete

   a ☐ × 0.07 = 7   **b** ☐ × 10 = 32   **c** ☐ × 100 = 946

   d 0.8 × ☐ = 800   **e** ☐ × 100 = 14.4   **f** 371 ÷ ☐ = 37.1

   g 42 ÷ ☐ = 0.42   **h** ☐ ÷ 10 = 0.8   **i** ☐ ÷ 100 = 5.71

2 A shopkeeper orders 1000 pencils at £0.23 each. How much does the shopkeeper pay in total?

3 Copy and complete each number chain below.

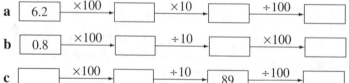

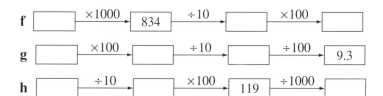

f ☐ →×1000→ 834 →÷10→ ☐ →×100→ ☐

g ☐ →×100→ ☐ →÷10→ ☐ →÷100→ 9.3

h ☐ →÷10→ ☐ →×100→ 119 →÷1000→ ☐

4 £3800 is shared between 1000 children. How much does each child get?

5 A cyclist travels 2.54 m in one second. How far does the cyclist travel in 100 seconds?

HWK 5M ────────────────────────────── **Main Book page 26**

Work out the following. (Check each answer by estimating)

1 2.7 × 6   **2** 0.14 × 3   **3** 4.81 × 5   **4** 8 × 0.53

5 12.3 × 9   **6** 4 × 3.46   **7** 2.718 × 7   **8** 5 × 0.049

9 8 × 21.84   **10** 3.783 × 6   **11** 31.87 × 9   **12** 12 × 6.8

13 A computer game costs £8.65 in a second-hand shop. How much would five of these games cost in this shop?

14 What is the cost of 8 scarves at £9.85 each?

15 Find each missing number.

    a ☐ × 8 = 4.8   **b** ☐ × 0.15 = 0.45   **c** ☐ × 9 − 9 = 4.5   **d** 12 = ☐ × 8 + 4.8

HWK 5E ────────────────────────────── **Main Book page 27**

1 Find the total cost of 6 pineapples at £1.84 each.

2 A tin of soup weighs 0.47 kg. How much will 9 tins weigh?

3 If 1 kg equals 2.2 pounds, how many pounds does a 5 kg sack of potatoes weigh?

4

    5 tins of beans at £0.49 each

    3 pints of milk at 47p per pint

    1 loaf of bread at £1.06

How much does Sonia spend on this shopping?

5 How much change from £30 will
Dylan get when he buys this shopping?

2 boxes of cereal at £1.93 per box

$\frac{1}{2}$ kg of apples at 92 p per kg

3 bottles of wine at £7.14 per bottle

6 bags of crisps at 38 p per bag

6 Copy and complete

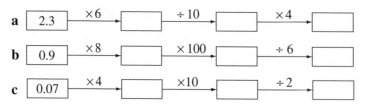

a 2.3 ─×6─→ ☐ ─÷10─→ ☐ ─×4─→ ☐

b 0.9 ─×8─→ ☐ ─×100─→ ☐ ─÷6─→ ☐

c 0.07 ─×4─→ ☐ ─×10─→ ☐ ─÷2─→ ☐

7 A shirt costs £22.50. Each shirt is given a logo for an extra £6.15. A school buys 20 shirts with logos. What is the total cost?

8 A family drinks 1.3 litres of milk each day. How many 2 litre bottles of milk will they buy during the entire month of October?

9 If £1 is equivalent to 1.25 euros, how many euros will Nadine take on holiday if she exchanges £250?

10

5 cm

3 cm

6.18 cm

The volume of a cuboid is length × width × height
What is the volume of this cuboid?

11 The sum of three consecutive numbers is 75. List the three numbers.

12 Work out $(7^2 - 10) \times (0.83 - 0.19 + 0.06 + 3)$

HWK 6M/6E | **Main Book page 28**

1 Work out

a 25.95 ÷ 5	**b** 51.2 ÷ 4	**c** 12.84 ÷ 3	**d** 226.1 ÷ 7
e 108.2 ÷ 5	**f** 71.12 ÷ 8	**g** 60.4 ÷ 4	**h** 31.6 ÷ 5
i 2507.4 ÷ 6			

2 A prize of £409.50 is shared equally between 6 people. How much will each person receive?

3   4 people buy a wedding present for a friend. The present costs £114.40 and the 4 people each pay an equal share. How much do they each pay?

4   A sheet of metal weighing 51.2 kg is to be divided into 8 equal parts.
How much will each part weigh?

5   10.7 litres of paint are poured equally into 5 tins. How much paint is in each tin?

6   Which answer below is the odd one out?

     A $3.72 \div 3$ **B** $7.56 \div 6$ **C** $8.68 \div 7$

7   Each of 3 triplets weigh the same amount. If their total weight is 154.8 kg, how much do each of the triplets weigh?

8   Which answer below is the odd one out?

     A $25.496 \div 8$ **B** $28.647 \div 9$ **C** $22.281 \div 7$

9   The total bill for a meal is £130. Eight people agree to pay an equal share. How much does each person pay?

10   Which is larger and by how much?

     P $96.8 \div 22$ **Q** $164.5 \div 35$

HWK 7M/7E   **Main Book page 30**

1   Work out

     a 0.6×0.4 **b** 0.8×0.07 **c** 6×0.09 **d** 0.9×8

     e 7×0.05 **f** 0.02×0.3 **g** 16×0.04 **h** 0.8×21

     i 1.8×0.6 **j** 0.07×0.04 **k** 0.32×0.5 **l** 0.003×1.3

2   Copy and complete

     a $7 \times 0.03 = \square$ **b** $0.8 \times \square = 0.16$ **c** $0.04 \times \square = 0.28$

     d $\square \times 0.6 = 0.042$ **e** $\square \times 0.03 = 0.012$ **f** $0.07 \times \square = 6.3$

3   Cheddar cheese costs £4.20 per kg. Ken buys 0.6 kg of cheese. How much does Ken pay?

4   A table at a local snooker club costs £5.30 per hour to hire. Simon and Denise play snooker for 1 hour 24 minutes. How much do they pay for the table? (1 hour 24 minutes = 1.4 hours)

5 Di has 15 prints each being a square of area 0.16 m². She needs to put frame around the edge of each print. What total length of wooden frame will she need for all 15 prints?

0.16 m²

6 Work out

    a 0.3^2 **b** 0.7^2 **c** $0.8^2 - 0.6^2$ **d** 0.2^3

7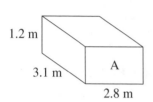

volume of cuboid
= length × width × height

Which cuboid has the larger volume and by how much?

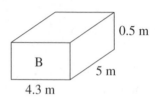

1.4 Using a calculator

HWK 1M ⎯⎯⎯⎯⎯⎯⎯⎯⎯⎯⎯⎯⎯⎯⎯⎯⎯⎯⎯⎯⎯⎯ **Main Book page 35**

Work out

1 $8 - 3 \times 2$ **2** $5 + 4 \times 3$ **3** $7 + 4 \times 6$

4 $3 \times 5 + 4$ **5** $7 \times 9 - 9$ **6** $8 \times 6 - 7$

7 $7 + 12 \div 3$ **8** $8 + 16 \div 2$ **9** $15 - 9 \div 3$

10 $30 \div 6 + 7$ **11** $45 \div 9 - 4$ **12** $28 + 4 \times 11$

13 $15 + 28 \div 7$ **14** $7 \times 8 + 17$ **15** $54 \div 6 - 5$

16 Copy and fill in each box to give the correct answer.

    a $5 \times \square + 2 = 22$ **b** $\square \times 7 - 6 = 15$ **c** $6 + 10 \div \square = 8$

    d $\square + 3 \times 8 = 29$ **e** $(8 - \square) \times 7 = 28$ **f** $15 \div (1 + \square) = 3$

    g $30 \div \square + 4 = 9$ **h** $(\square + 8) \times 6 = 66$ **i** $16 + 18 \div \square = 25$

HWK 1E ⎯⎯⎯⎯⎯⎯⎯⎯⎯⎯⎯⎯⎯⎯⎯⎯⎯⎯⎯⎯⎯⎯ **Main Book page 36**

Work out

1 $3 + 5 \times 7 + 4$ **2** $28 - 3 \times 6 + 4$ **3** $5 + 20 \div 5 + 3$

4 $12 - 30 \div 6 - 2$ **5** $27 \div 9 + 3 \times 6$ **6** $42 \div 7 - 36 \div 6$

7 $48 - 6 \times 7 + 9$ **8** $8 \times 9 \div 3 + 7$ **9** $7 \times 9 - 54 \div 9$

10 $(8 - 2) \times 8$ **11** $56 \div (9 - 2)$ **12** $(6 + 4) \times (15 - 8)$

13 $(13 + 11) \div (12 - 6)$ **14** $9 \times (24 - 15)$ **15** $5 \times 9 - 4 \times 7$

16 $72 \div 8 + 3 \times 7$ **17** $(14 + 6) \times (7 - 4)$ **18** $17 + 49 \div 7 - 16$

19 $200 - (36 \div 3)$ **20** $40 \div 8 + 4 \times 9$ **21** $7 \times 6 + (120 - 39)$

22 $\dfrac{16 - 7}{3}$ **23** $(7 + 19 + 4) \div (19 - 4)$ **24** $(28 - 6) \times (4 + 3)$

25 $\dfrac{5 + 5 \times 6}{7}$ **26** $(73 - 4) \div (48 - 5 \times 5)$ **27** $\dfrac{8 + 6 \div 3}{3 \times 2 - 1}$

28 $\dfrac{8 + 4 \times 9}{3 + 2 \times 4}$ **29** $\dfrac{(8 + 7) \times (5 - 2)}{3 \times (9 - 6)}$ **30** $\dfrac{(15 - 5) \div (2 + 3)}{16 - 7 \times 2}$

HWK 2M ———————————————————————————— **Main Book page 37**

Copy each question and write brackets so that each calculation gives the correct answer.

1 $4 + 3 \times 6 = 42$ **2** $5 \times 4 - 1 = 15$ **3** $7 + 5 \times 6 = 37$

4 $56 \div 10 - 2 = 7$ **5** $5 \times 4 + 2 \times 6 = 32$ **6** $8 \times 7 - 2 - 9 = 31$

7 $13 + 12 \div 5 = 5$ **8** $18 + 18 - 8 \div 4 = 7$ **9** $4 \times 6 + 9 - 5 = 40$

10 $42 - 6 \times 6 = 6$ **11** $15 + 6 \times 3 + 7 = 40$ **12** $24 - 9 \div 27 \div 9 = 5$

13 $41 + 22 \div 3 + 6 = 7$ **14** $8 + 10 \times 0 + 6 = 6$ **15** $58 - 4 \div 48 \div 8 = 9$

Work out questions **16** to **30**

16 4^3 **17** $3^2 - 7$ **18** $7 + 7^2$

19 6×5^2 **20** $(5 - 2)^3$ **21** $6^2 \times 3$

22 $1^3 \times 4$ **23** $(6 + 3)^2$ **24** $8 \times (9 - 6)^2$

25 $5 \times (2^2 + 2^2)$ **26** $(3 + 2)^2 - (6 - 4)^2$ **27** $(8^2 - 9) \times 2$

28 $3^3 - 6 \times 2$ **29** $(2^3 - 5) \times (8 - 4)$ **30** $40 \div (7 - 5)^3$

HWK 2E — — — — — — — — — — — — — — — — **Main Book page 38**

$(7 - 3) \times 8 = 32$ so the answer 32 can be found by using the numbers 7, 3 and 8.

For each question below, use each number once to give the correct answer. Write down the calculation each time.

1 8, 6 and 3 to give answer 6

2 7, 3 and 6 to give answer 60

3 5, 3 and 9 to give answer 30

4 10, 32 and 2 to give answer 4

5 9, 8 and 4 to give answer 44

6 3, 10 and 7 to give answer 100

7 4, 48 and 12 to give answer 6

8 64, 6 and 2 to give answer 8

9 3, 9 and 5 to give answer 72

10 28, 3 and 21 to give answer 4

11 5, 2, 20 and 1 to give answer 3

12 2, 3, 5 and 9 to give answer 42

13 1, 2, 5 and 6 to give answer 30

14 2, 3, 4 and 7 to give answer 54

15 Make up five questions of your own like these. You may use as many numbers as you like. Try them on other people in your next lesson.

HWK 3M — — — — — — — — — — — — — — — — **Main Book page 38**

Use a calculator to work out:

1 3.2×0.78

2 $5.12 + 3.4 - 0.79$

3 $2.6 \times 1.7 + 5.8$

4 $\dfrac{2.808}{1.3}$

5 $\dfrac{7.704}{0.02}$

6 $8.9 - 4.26 + 6.5$

7 Spencer buys seven CDs at £13.49 each. How much does he spend in total?

8 Polly buys 3 magazines at £2.95 each and 4 bottles of water at £1.07 each. How much does she spend in total?

9 Tom weighs 13 stone. Each stone is 14 pounds. Tom is a 'good' weight if he weighs less than 190 pounds. Is Tom a 'good' weight?

10 The answers for $2 + \dfrac{1.5}{0.25}$ and $\dfrac{2 + 1.5}{0.25}$ are 14 and 8. Which answer belongs to which calculation?

11 $5.3 + \dfrac{18.27}{2.9}$

12 $3.92 + 4.3 \times 2.6$

13 $\dfrac{6.41 + 9.55}{3.8}$

14 $\dfrac{1.9 \times 2.4}{0.04}$

15 $4.6 + \dfrac{27.44}{4.9}$

16 $\dfrac{29.732 - 3.94}{4.16}$

17 $7.16 - \dfrac{35.1}{7.8}$

18 $4.8 + 2.6 \times 2.9$

19 $\dfrac{8.513 + 3.793}{8.79}$

HWK 3E ——————————————————————————— **Main Book page 40**

Use a calculator to complete this crossnumber.

1		2			3	
				4		
5			6			
		7		8		9
10						
11	12		13			
14						

Across

1. $\dfrac{1505}{0.2} - 39$

3. $(0.15 + 0.35) \times (70 - 8)$

4. $(2.19 - 0.44) \times 8$

5. $1172.5 + (10251 \div 2)$

7. $\dfrac{12105}{0.4} + \dfrac{137052}{8}$

11. $(4 + 5) \times 4$

13. $3 \times (893.5 + 516.5) + 909$

14. $15455 \div (3.719 - 1.219)$

Down

1. $179 \times (2.16 + 1.84)$

2. $19445 + \dfrac{37500}{(0.7 - 0.1)}$

3. $\dfrac{2458}{(0.61 + 0.19)} + \dfrac{2852}{(3.2 + 4.8)}$

6. $290 \times (0.08 + 0.22)$

8. $(24.8 - 8.72 + 2.92) \times 19$

9. $(2107 + 1324) \times 2 - 1966$

10. $\dfrac{(113 + 96)}{(0.5 \times 0.5)}$

12. $\dfrac{(13.2 + 1.8)}{(0.29 - 0.04)} + 1$

13. $\dfrac{41.6}{0.8}$

HWK 4M/4E ——————————————————————— **Main Book page 42**

Work out each answer with a calculator. Write down all the numbers in your calculator display.

1 $17.6 - \left(\dfrac{15.3}{6.4}\right)$

2 $\dfrac{23.8}{4.9 + 5.62}$

3 $\dfrac{7.4}{3.1} + \dfrac{6.7}{10.3}$

4 $\quad 5.3^2 - \dfrac{6.4}{2.8}$

5 $\quad \dfrac{17.9 - 5.63}{2.16 + 5.4}$

6 $\quad \dfrac{23.5 - 4.82}{3.6^2}$

7 $\quad \dfrac{8.2}{2.1} + \dfrac{3.7}{5.4} + \dfrac{7.2}{1.9}$

8 $\quad \left(12.9 - \dfrac{4.2}{2.83}\right)^2 \times 1.8$

9 $\quad 9.5^2 + 3.1^2 \times 4.9^2$

10 $\quad \sqrt{(6.7^2 - 19.2)}$

11 $\quad \dfrac{5.82^2}{4.61 + 2.8}$

12 $\quad 6.2^2 + \sqrt{(15.7 - 2.8)}$

13 A pile of 63 tiles is 49.14 cm high. How thick is each tile?

14 A motorist does 17226 miles a year in a car which does 43.5 miles per gallon. Petrol costs £4.95 per gallon. What is the total cost of the petrol used by the motorist during this year?

15
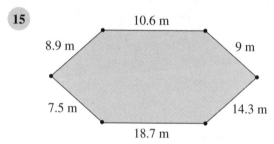

This field has a fence around its perimeter. The fence costs £12.35 per metre. Find the total cost for the whole fence.

16 Work out each calculation below and write down the first three digits of each answer.

$$\dfrac{31848 - 187.04}{0.3^2 + 7.91} \qquad 21.7^2 - \dfrac{2}{0.5^2} \qquad \dfrac{7.6 - 2.1^2}{0.8^2 - 0.62^2}$$

Find the sum of the nine digits then square root the answer. Write down this final answer.

1.5 Sequences

HWK 1M/1E ———————————————— **Main Book page 45**

In questions **1** to **9** write down the next 2 terms in each sequence.

1 $\quad 6, 5\frac{1}{2}, 5, 4\frac{1}{2}, ..$

2 $\quad 1.4, 1.7, 2, 2.3, ..$

3 $\quad 4, 2, 0, -2, -4, ..$

4 $\quad 4, 5, 7, 10, 14, ..$

5 $\quad 12, 23, 34, 45, ..$

6 $\quad 256, 64, 16, 4, ..$

7 $\quad 5, 15, 45, 135, ..$

8 $\quad 1, 3, 6, 10, 15, ..$

9 $\quad 400, 40, 4, 0.4, ..$

10 Each year Maggie gets a £550 pay rise. At end of 2007 she earns £16100. How much will she earn at the end of 2011?

11 Write down each sequence and find the missing numbers.

    a 64, 32, ☐, 8, 4   **b** ☐, 8, ☐, 18, 23   **c** 31, 25, ☐, 13, ☐   **d** 1.5, ☐, 2, 2.25, ☐

12

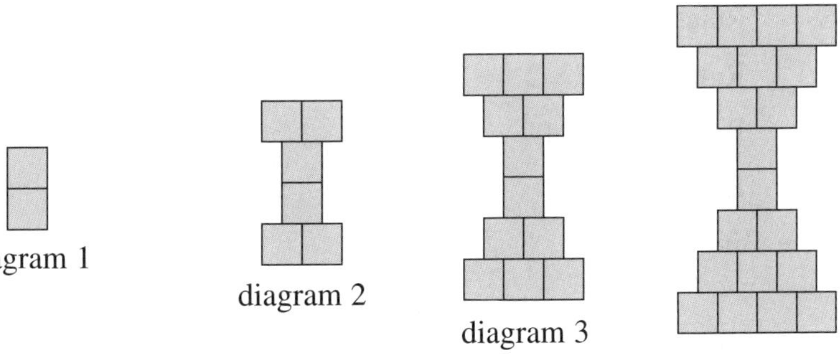

diagram 1

diagram 2

diagram 3

diagram 4

These diagrams form a sequence.

a How many squares in diagram 5?

b How many squares in diagram 10? *Explain* your answer.

In questions **13** to **15** copy each alphabet sequence and write down the next 2 letters.

13 a, c, e, g, ..   **14** a, b, d, g, ..   **15** h, k, n, q, ..

16 Finally, write down the next term in each of these sequences.

a | 4 | 4 | 8 | 24 | 96 | ☐ |

b | 0 | 5 | 12 | 21 | 32 | ☐ |

c | 2 | 7 | 22 | 67 | 202 | ☐ |

HWK 2M ———————————————————————— **Main Book page 46**

1 You are given the first term and the rule of several sequences. Write down the first 4 terms of each sequence.

	First term	Rule
a	9	add 3
b	73	subtract 6
c	96	divide by 2
d	5	double

24

2 Find the first five terms of each sequence.

    a 2nd term = 14   Rule: add 6

    b 3rd term = 48   Rule: multiply by 4

    c 2nd term = 40   Rule: divide by 2

    d 5th term = 17   Rule: subtract 4

    e 4th term = 4.6   Rule: add 0.3

3 Here is a sequence using matches.

  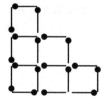

Draw the next picture in the sequence and write down how many matches are used.

4 Write down the rule for each of these sequences.

    a 93, 81, 69, 57   **b** 243, 81, 27, 9   **c** –2, – 3, – 4, – 5

    d 7, 14, 28, 56, 112   **e** 3, 5, 15, 65, 315   **f** 4, 5, 9, 14, 23

5 The rule for the sequences below is '*multiply by 2 and subtract 1*'. Copy each sequence and find the missing numbers.

    a $3 \rightarrow 5 \rightarrow 9 \rightarrow 17 \rightarrow \square$

    b $\square \rightarrow 15 \rightarrow 29 \rightarrow 57$

    c $\square \rightarrow 7 \rightarrow \square \rightarrow \square$

HWK 2E   **Main Book page 48**

1 Write down 5 terms of a sequence with the rule 'subtract 8' where none of the terms is a whole number.

2 Find the missing numbers for each sequence.

    a   28   Rule: subtract 5

    b 18   Rule: multiply by 3

    c 14   Rule: divide by 2

3 Copy this pattern and write down the next three lines. Do not use a calculator!

$$1 \times 99 = 99$$
$$2 \times 99 = 198$$
$$3 \times 99 = 297$$
$$4 \times 99 = 396$$

4 The following are linear sequences (the terms go up or go down in equal steps).

a
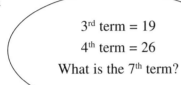
3rd term = 19
4th term = 26
What is the 7th term?

b
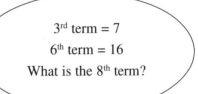
3rd term = 7
6th term = 16
What is the 8th term?

c
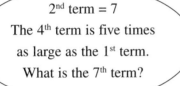
2nd term = 7
The 4th term is five times
as large as the 1st term.
What is the 7th term?

d
1st term = 20
The 4th term is the
lowest prime number.
What is the 6th term?

5 Jan has 4 gerbils at the end of July. Each month the number of gerbils trebles but 6 gerbils die. At the end of which month will there be 84 gerbils?!

6 **a** Copy this pattern and write down the next two lines.

$$4 \times 8 = 32$$
$$44 \times 8 = 352$$
$$444 \times 8 = 3552$$
$$4444 \times 8 = 35552$$

b Copy and complete 444 444 444 × 8 =

7 Find the missing numbers for each sequence.

a   31   Rule: multiply by 2 then add 1

b 7   Rule: multiply by 4 then subtract 5

1.6 Perimeter and area

1 What is the perimeter of a square with each side 7 cm?

2 **a** Which shape below has the larger perimeter – the square with side 13 cm or the rectangle 17.5 cm by 7.5 cm?

b Write down the difference between the perimeters of the square and rectangle above.

3 The perimeter of a rectangular swimming pool is 74 m. What is the length of the pool if the width is 12 m?

4 Find the perimeter of each shape. The lengths are in cm.

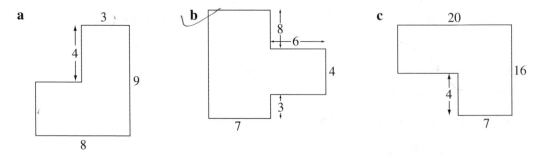

5 A rectangular picture has a perimeter of 296 cm. If its length is three times its width, what is the length of the picture?

6

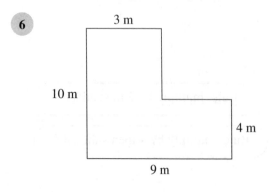

This is a plan of Neil's room. He wants to put coving around the perimeter of his room.
The coving comes in 4 m pieces. How many pieces of coving must Neil buy?

HWK 1E ———————————————————— **Main Book page 52**

1 What is the area of this lawn?
(The lawn is shaded.)

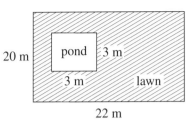

20 m pond 3 m
3 m lawn
22 m

2 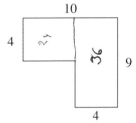 What is the perimeter of this square?

169 cm²

3 A rectangle has an area of 75 m². If the length is 10 m, what is its width?

4 Find the area of each shape. The lengths are in cm.

a

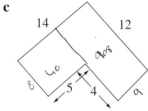

10
4
36
9
4

b

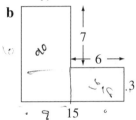

7
6
.3
9 15

c

14 12
40
5 4
8 9

d

3
5
14 98 35
5
4
7

5 Find each shaded area (the lengths are in cm).

a

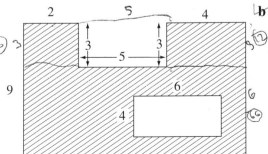

2 5 4
3 3
5
9 6
4

b

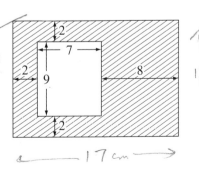

2
7
2
9 8 13
2
17 cm

6

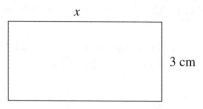

16 cm

6 cm

These two rectangles have the same area. Find the value of *x*.

x

3 cm

7 Shannon wants to carpet her living room and dining room. What is the total area of carpet she will need?

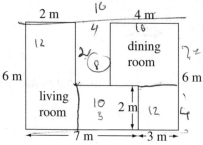

2 m   16   4 m

12   4   16

6 m   2⊘   dining room   7 z

8

living room   10   2 m   12

3   7 m   3 m

8 Amy is putting tiles on part of her kitchen wall shown below. Each tile is 15 cm by 10 cm. How many tiles will she use if she does not break any?

0.9 m

0.⊔   22m   0.3   34

0.4 m

0.3   9m   0.1 m   9m   0.3

0.3 m   0.3m   0.3 m

1 Find the area of a triangle with a base of 16 m and a height of 9 m.

2 Find the total area of each shape. Lengths are in cm.

a

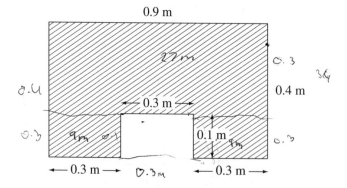

12

7   8

48   96

b

63

6   16

19

3

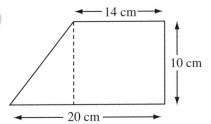

These two shapes have the same area. Find the value of x.

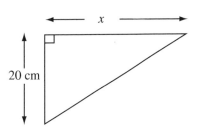

4 Find the height of a triangle with a base of 30 m and an area of 45 m².

5 Find the total area of each shape. Lengths are in cm.

a

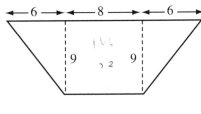

b

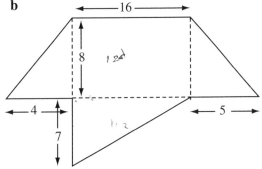

6 Find the total shaded area. Lengths are in cm.

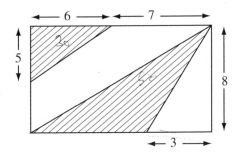

7

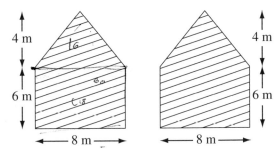

Denise is painting both ends of her house. Each pot of paint will cover 15 m². How many pots of paint will Denise need?

30

8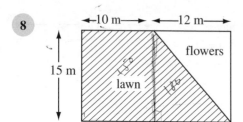

Calculate the area of the lawn.

9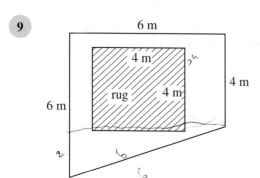

This diagram shows a room with a rug 4 m by 4 m.

a What is the total area of the room?
b What is the area of the rug?
c What area of the floor is *not* covered by the rug?

HWK 2E ──────────────────────────── **Main Book page 57**

1 Find the area of each shape.

a 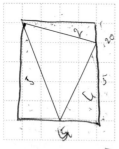 **b** 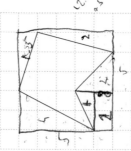 **c**

2 For each question, draw two axes from 0 to 7. Plot the points given and join them up in order. Find the area of each shape.

a (0, 3), (3, 6), (5, 5), (2, 1)   **b** (1, 3), (3, 6), (7, 5), (4, 3), (3, 1)

3 Do the same as question **2** with the two axes drawn from 0 to 10.

(0, 3), (2, 7), (4, 9), (8, 7), (6, 3), (2, 1)

HWK 3M/3E ──────────────────────────── **Main Book page 58**

(Note that 10000 m² = 1 hectare)

1 A wall measuring 5.5 m by 2.5 m is to be covered by square tiles measuring 50 cm by 50 cm. How many tiles are needed?

2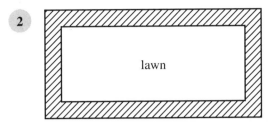

A lawn measures 18 m by 12 m.
It is surrounded by a path 1.5 m wide.
What is the area of the path?

3 A rectangular field 750 m long has an area of 3 hectares. Calculate the width of the field.

4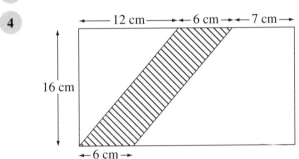

A flag has a sloping strip drawn across.
Calculate the area of the shaded strip.

5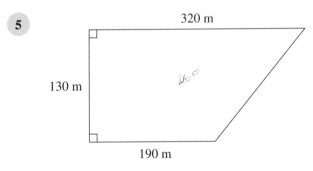

A farmer sprays this field. Each bottle
of spray covers 650 m². Each bottle
costs £10.68.
How much will the farmer pay to spray
the entire field?

6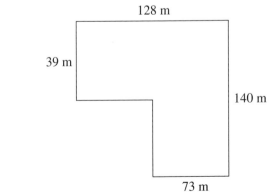

This plot of land is sold at £2700 per hectare.
How much does the plot cost?

7 A park has an area of two hectares. It contains two football pitches, each measuring 92 m by 53 m, and three hockey pitches, each measuring 64 m by 30 m.

What area of the park is not covered by a football or hockey pitch?

8   A rectangular field has a perimeter of 540 m and a length of 200 m. What is its area in hectares?

9

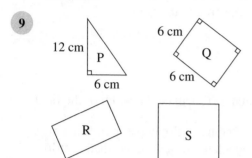

The area of square S is double the area of rectangle R. The area of square S is equal to the sum of the areas of shapes P, Q and R. Find the length of the side of square S.

10

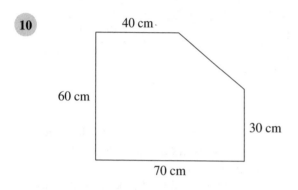

Max is going to tile this section of a wall with square tiles measuring 10 cm by 10 cm. When he cuts a tile in half he only uses one half of that tile. What is the least number of tiles he will use?

UNIT 2

HWK 1M ——————————————————— **Main Book page 73**

For each list of numbers in questions **1** to **4**, find **a** the mean, **b** the median, **c** the mode and **d** the range.

1 3, 7, 9, 5, 3, 9, 9, 2, 7, 9, 3

2 120, 110, 108, 112, 120

3 15, 11, 13, 19, 13, 15, 11, 15

4 8, 5, 7, 3, 9, 1, 3, 4, 3, 7

5 The total weight of 7 children is 294 kg. Find the mean weight of the children.

6

4, 6, 6, 5, 7, 5, 4
6, 5, 8, 6, 4, 8, 5
4, 5, 7, 5, 6, 7, 4
7, 8, 5, 6, 5, 4, 7

The shoe sizes of a class of 28 pupils are shown in this box. Find the modal shoe size (the mode).

7 The ages of some dogs in a kennel were 7, 3, 5, 3, 10, 2 and the ages of some cats were 5, 6, 9, 8.

   a Find the mean age for the dogs.
   b Find the mean age for the cats.
   c Find the mean age for all ten animals.

8 'The modes for the numbers 3, 3, 3, 4, 4, 5, 5, 6, 6, 6, 7, 7, 7, 8 are 3, 6 and 7.'
   Is this true or false?

HWK 1E ——————————————————— **Main Book page 74**

1 Callum throws a dice eight times and his grandfather gives him a £1 coin if the mean score is equal to 3. The dice are shown below.

   Does he win £1?

2 Meg has five discs.
The mean of the five discs is 8.
The range of the five discs is 4.
What numbers are on the other two discs?

(8) (8) (8) ( ) ( )

3 | 9 | | 13 | | 7 | | 5 | | 16 | | | Ben has six cards. The mean of the six cards is equal to 9. What is the missing number?

4 There were 9 people in a rowing team. The mean age of the people was 22 and the range of their ages was 6.

Write each sentence below and write next to it whether it is *True, Possible* or *Impossible*.

a Every person was 22 years old.
b All the people were at least 20 years old.
c The oldest person was 6 years older than the youngest person.
d The youngest person on the boat was 14 years old.

5 Claire has 2 older sisters and 2 older brothers. The total age of the five children is 64 years. There are two modes of 12 and 15.

a How old is Claire?   **b** Write down the median age.

6 | List A: −4   −8   2   −5   0   −7 |

| List B: 3   −1   −6   4   −3   −4 |

Which list has the higher median and by how much?

7 | 3 | | 8 | | 7 | | 4 | | 8 | + | ? |

The mean value for these cards increases by 1 when the mystery card is added to the other 5 cards. What is the value on the mystery card?

8 A group of 7 people pick a mean average of 1582 strawberries each one day. A different group of 5 people pick a mean average of 2214 strawberries.

Which group of people picked the most strawberries on that day? How many more strawberries did they pick?

HWK 2E ———————————————————— **Main Book page 76**

1 Eleven children in Year 7 and eleven children in Year 10 were asked how many pints of milk they drank in an 'average' week. The results are recorded below:

Year 7: 2 5 3 7 5 0 1 4 0 2 5

Year 10: 9 3 2 6 9 5 7 0 5 2 12

a Work out the median and range for Year 7.

b Work out the median and range for Year 10.

c Copy and complete the statement below:

'The median for Year 7 is (greater/smaller) than the median for Year 10 and the range for Year 7 is (greater/smaller) than the range for Year 10. This means the results for Year 7 are (more/less) spread out.'

2 The charts below show how many goals were scored in football matches one weekend in the Premiership and in the Championship.

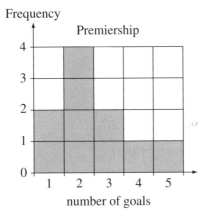
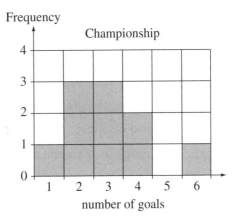

a Work out the mean and range for the Premiership.

b Work out the mean and range for the Championship.

c Write a sentence to compare the number of goals scored in the Premiership and in the Championship.

HWK 2M ———————————————————— **Main Book page 78**

1 The table below shows the number of televisions in each of 50 houses.

number of televisions	0	1	2	3	4	5	6
number of houses	3	9	16	6	10	5	1

Copy and complete: mean number of televisions $= \dfrac{(3 \times 0) + (9 \times 1) + \ldots}{50} = \dfrac{\square}{50} = \square$.

2 80 people were asked how many pints of water they drink each day. The results are shown in the table below.

number of pints	1	2	3	4	5
number of people	26	23	18	7	6

a Find the modal number of pints drunk each day.

b Find the mean number of pints drunk each day.

ng one season, two football teams play 40 matches. The number of goals they scored in
match is shown in the tables below.

Hatton Albion

number of goals	0	1	2	3	4	5
number of matches	4	9	18	6	2	1

Carrow City

number of goals	0	1	2	3	4	5
number of matches	13	5	7	9	4	2

a Find the mean average number of goals scored by each team.

b Which team had the higher mean average and by how much?

4 The ages of 15 people in a Youth Orchestra are shown below.

age (in years)	12	13	14	15	16	17
frequency	4	1	4	2	2	2

a Find the mean age.

b One person leaves the Orchestra and the mean age drops to 14.
How old was the person who left the Orchestra?

2.2 Fractions

HWK 1M ──────────────────── **Main Book page 81**

1 Find the missing number to make these fractions equivalent.

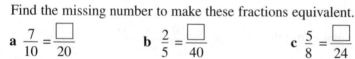

a $\dfrac{7}{10} = \dfrac{\square}{20}$ **b** $\dfrac{2}{5} = \dfrac{\square}{40}$ **c** $\dfrac{5}{8} = \dfrac{\square}{24}$ **d** $\dfrac{1}{7} = \dfrac{\square}{35}$

e $\dfrac{8}{9} = \dfrac{24}{\square}$ **f** $\dfrac{3}{8} = \dfrac{27}{\square}$ **g** $\dfrac{5}{6} = \dfrac{\square}{48}$ **h** $\dfrac{2}{11} = \dfrac{8}{\square}$

i $\dfrac{7}{20} = \dfrac{21}{\square}$ **j** $\dfrac{9}{100} = \dfrac{36}{\square}$ **k** $\dfrac{16}{25} = \dfrac{\square}{75}$ **l** $\dfrac{7}{15} = \dfrac{\square}{75}$

2 Write down which fractions are equal to $\frac{2}{3}$.

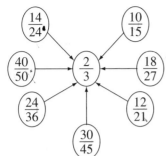

3 Copy and find the missing numbers to make these fractions equivalent.

a $\frac{7}{12} = \frac{\square}{24} = \frac{21}{\square}$

b $\frac{7}{9} = \frac{\square}{54} = \frac{49}{\square}$

c $\frac{\square}{3} = \frac{6}{18} = \frac{\square}{15}$

d $\frac{3}{24} = \frac{\square}{32} = \frac{\square}{8}$

4

A	D	E	F	H	I	K	M	N	O	R	S	V	W	Y
$\frac{1}{3}$	$\frac{2}{5}$	$\frac{5}{9}$	$\frac{4}{5}$	$\frac{3}{7}$	$\frac{5}{12}$	$\frac{1}{6}$	$\frac{3}{8}$	$\frac{1}{4}$	$\frac{5}{6}$	$\frac{11}{20}$	$\frac{3}{4}$	$\frac{1}{8}$	$\frac{7}{10}$	$\frac{4}{9}$

Cancel each fraction below and select the letter from the table above to make a sentence.

$\frac{15}{36}$ $\frac{18}{42}$ $\frac{7}{21}$ $\frac{4}{32}$ $\frac{40}{72}$ $\frac{12}{15}$ $\frac{20}{48}$ $\frac{9}{36}$ $\frac{45}{108}$ $\frac{24}{32}$ $\frac{9}{21}$ $\frac{35}{63}$ $\frac{20}{50}$

$\frac{36}{96}$ $\frac{60}{135}$ $\frac{24}{56}$ $\frac{30}{36}$ $\frac{60}{160}$ $\frac{25}{45}$ $\frac{28}{40}$ $\frac{55}{66}$ $\frac{77}{140}$ $\frac{16}{96}$

HWK 1E ———————————————— **Main Book page 83**

Change the following improper fractions to mixed numbers or whole numbers only.

1 $\frac{11}{4}$

2 $\frac{10}{3}$

3 $\frac{7}{3}$ **4** $\frac{5}{4}$ **5** $\frac{15}{8}$ **6** $\frac{20}{4}$ **7** $\frac{16}{7}$ **8** $\frac{13}{5}$ **9** $\frac{47}{10}$

In questions **10** to **19** change the mixed numbers to improper fractions

10 $1\frac{3}{4}$ **11** $5\frac{1}{2}$ **12** $3\frac{5}{6}$ **13** $4\frac{3}{8}$ **14** $2\frac{3}{10}$

15 $3\frac{2}{5}$ **16** $6\frac{1}{4}$ **17** $2\frac{5}{8}$ **18** $5\frac{3}{7}$ **19** $8\frac{7}{10}$

20   How many quarters are there in $16\frac{1}{4}$?

21   How many thirds are there in $7\frac{2}{3}$?

22   Which fraction is the odd one out ?

$$\boxed{\frac{16}{6}} \qquad \boxed{2\frac{2}{3}} \qquad \boxed{\frac{64}{24}} \qquad \boxed{2\frac{9}{12}} \qquad \boxed{\frac{8}{3}}$$

HWK 2M ──────────────────────────────── **Main Book page 84**

1   There are 140 pupils in Year 7. If $\frac{3}{7}$ of the pupils are boys, how many girls are there?

2   Which is larger?

$$\left(\frac{5}{8} \text{ of } 56\right) \qquad \text{or} \qquad \left(\frac{6}{7} \text{ of } 42\right)$$

3   Full marks in a test were 65. How many marks did Zoe get if she scored $\frac{3}{5}$ of full marks?

4   Work out

   a $\frac{4}{7}$ of 350 kg   **b** $\frac{5}{6}$ of 72 cm   **c** $\frac{7}{9}$ of £135

   d $\frac{3}{8}$ of £176   **e** $\frac{7}{12}$ of 84 litres   **f** $\frac{9}{20}$ of 2600 kg

   g $\frac{4}{15}$ of 240 g   **h** $\frac{7}{11}$ of £132   **i** $\frac{13}{25}$ of £225

5   Gemma has £80. She spends $\frac{2}{5}$ of this money on a skirt. She spends $\frac{3}{4}$ of the remaining money on some trousers and spends half of the money she has left on a present for her brother. How much money does she now have left?

6   Find each missing number below

   a $\frac{\square}{3}$ of 27 = 18   **b** $\frac{4}{\square}$ of 35 = 28   **c** $\frac{\square}{9}$ of 36 = 20

   d $\frac{3}{4}$ of $\square$ = 36   **e** $\frac{\square}{8}$ of 24 = 21   **f** $\frac{5}{6}$ of $\square$ = 45

7   Henry's new jeans are 96 cm long. After washing they shrink to $\frac{11}{12}$ of their original length. What is the new length of the jeans?

8   Work out

   a $\frac{3}{5} \times 40$ **b** $24 \times \frac{5}{8}$ **c** $70 \times \frac{9}{10}$ **d** $\frac{5}{9} \times 63$

   e $42 \times \frac{6}{7}$ **f** $\frac{7}{20} \times 180$ **g** $\frac{8}{11} \times 121$ **h** $48 \times \frac{5}{6}$

9 A glass holds $\frac{5}{8}$ of a litre of liquid. How much liquid is contained in 16 glasses?

10 Work out $\frac{5}{8}$ of $\frac{2}{3}$ of 60

HWK 2E ——————————————————————————— **Main Book page 87**

1 Copy and complete: $\dfrac{9}{10} - \dfrac{3}{7} = \dfrac{\square}{70} - \dfrac{\square}{70} = \dfrac{\square}{70}$

In questions **2** to **13** , work out the answers and cancel if necessary

2 $\dfrac{1}{3} + \dfrac{2}{5}$ **3** $\dfrac{1}{4} + \dfrac{1}{7}$ **4** $\dfrac{3}{4} - \dfrac{1}{3}$ **5** $\dfrac{5}{6} - \dfrac{2}{5}$

6 $\dfrac{2}{9} + \dfrac{3}{7}$ **7** $\dfrac{7}{11} - \dfrac{5}{9}$ **8** $\dfrac{7}{8} - \dfrac{4}{5}$ **9** $\dfrac{1}{6} + \dfrac{3}{10}$

10 $\dfrac{7}{20} - \dfrac{1}{9}$ **11** $\dfrac{9}{16} + \dfrac{2}{5}$ **12** $\dfrac{2}{5} - \dfrac{3}{20}$ **13** $\dfrac{9}{10} - \dfrac{4}{7}$

14 In a class $\frac{1}{10}$ of the children cycle to school, $\frac{1}{3}$ of the children walk, $\frac{1}{5}$ come by car and the rest come by bus. What fraction of the class comes by bus?

15 Richard read $\frac{3}{8}$ of his book one day and $\frac{2}{5}$ the next day. What fraction of the book remains to be read?

16 Work out

a $5\frac{1}{4} - \frac{1}{5}$ **b** $2\frac{1}{2} + 1\frac{2}{3}$ **c** $2\frac{5}{6} + 3\frac{1}{2}$ **d** $3\frac{1}{4} - 1\frac{4}{5}$

17 A mechanic has a 5 litre can of oil. He pours $1\frac{2}{3}$ litres into the first car, $1\frac{1}{4}$ litres into the second car and $1\frac{1}{6}$ litres into the third car. How much oil is left in the can?

18 There are two routes from P to S. The 'safe' way is passing through Q and R. The 'dangerous' way is direct from P to S. How much shorter is it to take the 'dangerous' route?

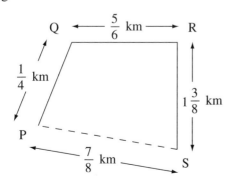

19 Matt is picking cabbages and putting them into a crate. At midday the crate is two-thirds full. At 1 p.m. he has added another 150 cabbages and the crate is $\frac{7}{8}$ full. How many more cabbage must he put into the crate to fill it completely?

20 Laura's petrol tank is $\frac{3}{4}$ full. On her next journey she uses 33 litres of petrol and finds out that her tank is now only $\frac{1}{5}$ full. How many litres must she put into her tank to fill it up completely?

2.3 Fractions, decimals, percentages

HWK 1M ———————————————————————————— **Main Book page 89**

Convert these fractions into decimals.

1 $\frac{19}{100}$ **2** $\frac{4}{5}$ **3** $\frac{12}{48}$ **4** $\frac{13}{20}$ **5** $\frac{24}{32}$

6 $\frac{13}{26}$ **7** $\frac{16}{25}$ **8** $\frac{180}{200}$ **9** $\frac{42}{56}$ **10** $\frac{11}{20}$

11   **a** Change $\frac{2}{6}$ into a recurring decimal.

     b Write $\frac{2}{60}$ as a recurring decimal.

12 Write $\frac{2}{300}$ as a recurring decimal.

HWK 1E ———————————————————————————— **Main Book page 90**

Convert these fractions into decimals.

1 $\frac{37}{1000}$ **2** $\frac{43}{500}$ **3** $\frac{290}{2000}$ **4** $\frac{3}{125}$ **5** $\frac{80}{320}$

6 $\frac{117}{250}$ **7** $\frac{90}{3000}$ **8** $\frac{135}{180}$ **9** $\frac{574}{10000}$ **10** $\frac{28}{125}$

11 Which is larger?

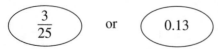

$\frac{3}{25}$ or   0.13

12 Which is larger?

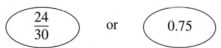

$\frac{24}{30}$ or   0.75

13 Write these numbers in order of size, smallest first

$\dfrac{18}{250}$ $\boxed{0.78}$ $\dfrac{14}{200}$ $\boxed{0.8}$

14 Write these numbers in order of size, smallest first.

$\dfrac{13}{52}$ $\dfrac{33}{125}$ $\boxed{0.304}$ $\boxed{0.24}$

HWK 2M/2E ───────────────────────── **Main Book page 90**

1 Write these decimals as fractions (cancel down fractions when possible).

a 0.6	**b** 0.08	**c** 0.28	**d** 0.45	**e** 0.34
f 0.65	**g** 0.25	**h** 0.14	**i** 0.2	**j** 0.76
k 5.4	**l** 3.24	**m** 5.85	**n** 8.75	**o** 2.16

2 Melissa has eaten 0.44 of her pizza. What fraction of her pizza is left? (cancel down the answer if possible)

3 Match up the creatures with the equivalent decimals and fractions.

a   **b**    **c**

d    **e**    **f**

g    **h** 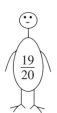   **i**    **j**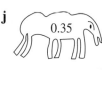

42

1 $80\% = \dfrac{80}{100} = \dfrac{4}{5}$ Change these percentages into fractions.

     a 90%   **b** 46%   **c** 13%   **d** 6%   **e** 45%

2   Copy and complete the following.

     a $\dfrac{7}{20} = \dfrac{35}{100} = \square\,\%$ **b** $\dfrac{17}{50} = \dfrac{\square}{100} = \square\,\%$

     c $\dfrac{3}{5} = \dfrac{\square}{100} = \square\,\%$ **d** $\dfrac{12}{25} = \dfrac{\square}{100} = \square\,\%$

3   Leona scored $\dfrac{16}{25}$ and Gary scored 65%. Who got the higher mark?

4   Tim is collecting football cards. He has collected $\dfrac{11}{20}$ of the cards. What percentage of the cards does he still need to collect?

5   Change each fraction below into a percentage then write out the fractions in order of size, starting with the smallest.

     $\dfrac{9}{20}$ $\dfrac{1}{2}$ $\dfrac{9}{25}$ $\dfrac{23}{50}$ $\dfrac{1}{3}$ $\dfrac{2}{5}$ $\dfrac{3}{10}$

1   Write these percentages as decimals.

     a 39%   **b** 38%   **c** 20%   **d** 29%   **e** 140%   **f** 375%

2   Copy and complete the following.

     a $0.61 = \dfrac{\square}{100} = \square\,\%$ **b** $0.6 = \dfrac{6}{10} = \dfrac{\square}{100} = \square\,\%$

     c $0.09 = \dfrac{\square}{100} = \square\,\%$ **d** $0.16 = \dfrac{\square}{100} = \square\,\%$

3   Mary, Lee and Todd are trying to lose weight. One week Mary loses 0.3 kg, Lee loses $\dfrac{8}{25}$ kg and Todd loses 31% of a kilogram. Who loses the most weight?

4   Which number is the odd one out?

     60% $\dfrac{12}{20}$ $\dfrac{1}{6}$ 0.6 $\dfrac{6}{10}$ 0.60 $\dfrac{3}{5}$

5 At a wedding, 74% of the wedding cake is eaten. 0.12 of the cake is kept to celebrate the first born baby. The rest of the cake is given to the bride's mother. What fraction of the cake is given to the bride's mother?

6 Copy and complete the table.

fraction	$\frac{13}{25}$					$\frac{13}{20}$	$\frac{9}{50}$	
decimal			0.19	0.24				
percentage		15%			26%			92%

2.4 Angles

HWK 1M ———————————————————————— **Main Book page 96**

Write down the size of each angle stated below:

1

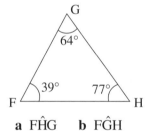

a FĤG b FĜH

2

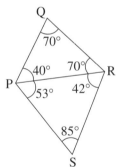

a PR̂S b SP̂R
c SP̂Q d QR̂S

3

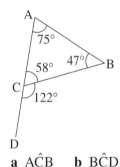

a AĈB b BĈD

4 Describe each angle listed below
(example: 105° is QP̂T)

a 32° b 62°
c 40° d 108°
e 73° f 48°

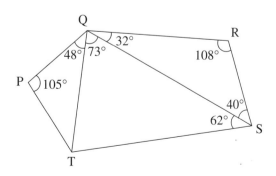

44

In questions **1** and **2** use large letters to indicate the angles shown by the small letters
(for example: a = RQ̂T).

1

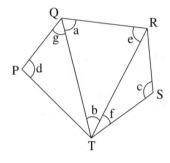

2

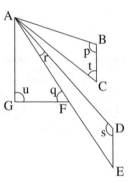

3 Use the diagram to give the value of each angle.

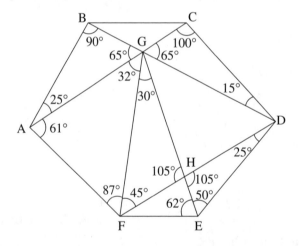

a AĜF	**b** FĜE
c AĜB	**d** BĜF
e DĤE	**f** BÂF
g AF̂G	**h** AĜH
i AF̂H	**j** DĈG
k BĜE	**l** DÊF

Use a protractor to draw the following angles accurately.

1

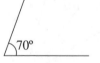

70°

2

140°

3 125°

4 35°

5 115°

6 58°   **7** 27°   **8** 132°   **9** 163°

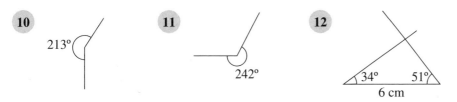

10 213°

11 242°

12 34° 51° 6 cm

13

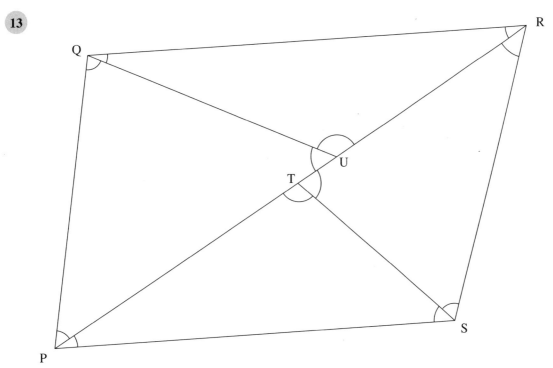

Use a protractor to measure these angles on the diagram above.

a PÛQ   **b** TR̂S   **c** RQ̂U   **d** QP̂U   **e** PŜR   **f** RT̂S

g QR̂S   **h** SP̂T   **i** RŜT   **j** PT̂S   **k** PQ̂R   **l** PŜT

HWK 3M/3E ———————————————————— **Main Book page 100**

Find the angles marked with letters.

1 a 155°

2 63° b

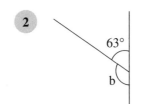

3 70° c 74°

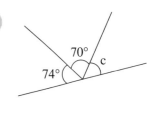

46

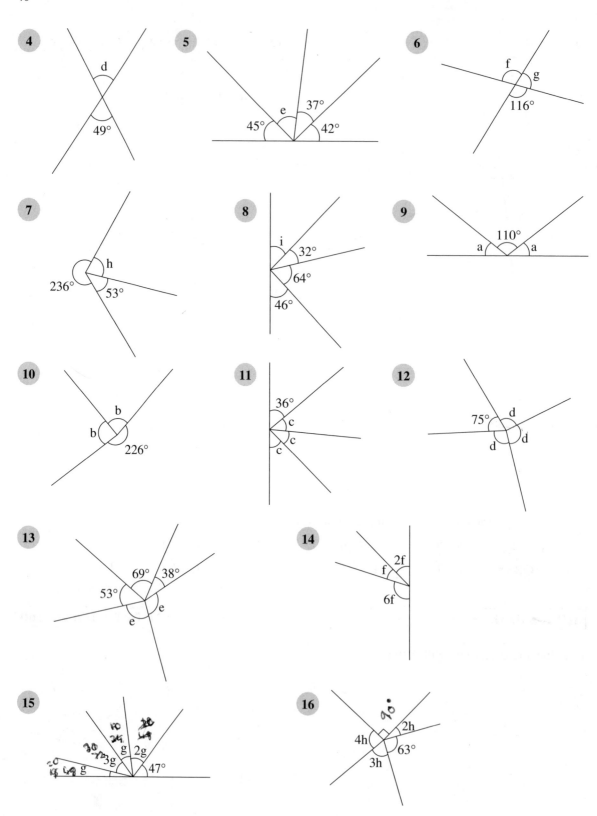

4 d 49°

5 45° e 37° 42°

6 f g 116°

7 236° h 53°

8 i 32° 64° 46°

9 110° a a

10 b b 226°

11 36° c c c

12 75° d d d

13 69° 38° 53° e e

14 2f f 6f

15 g 2g 3g g 47°

16 90° 2h 4h 63° 3h

47

HWK 4M

Main Book page 102

Find the angles marked with letters.

1
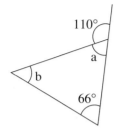
110°
a
b
66°

2
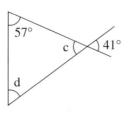
57°
c
41°
d

3
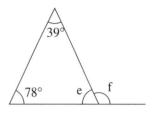
39°
78°
e
f

4
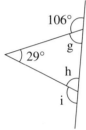
106°
29°
g
h
i

5
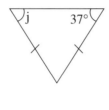
j
37°

6
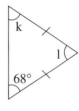
k
l
68°

7
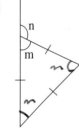
n
m

8
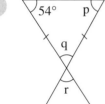
54°
p
q
r

9
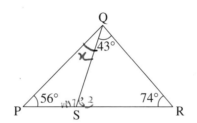
Q
43°
56°
S
74°
P
R

Find the value of PQ̂S

10
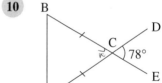
B
D
C
78°
E
A

Find the value of BÂC

HWK 4E

Main Book page 102

Find the angles marked with letters.

1
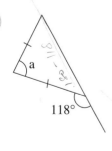
a
118°

2
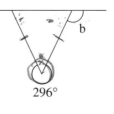
b
296°

3
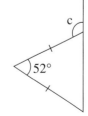
c
52°

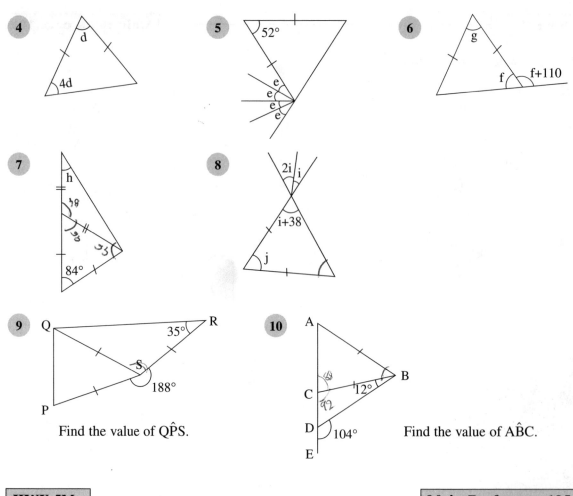

4 d, 4d

5 52°, e, e, e, e

6 g, f, f+110

7 h, 48, 84°, 35

8 2i, i, i+38, j

9 Q, R, 35°, S, 188°, P

Find the value of QP̂S.

10 A, C, 12°, B, D, 104°, E

Find the value of AB̂C.

HWK 5M	Main Book page 105

Find the angles marked with letters.

1 115°, a, b, c

2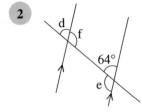
d, f, 64°, e

3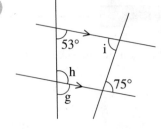
53°, i, h, g, 75°

4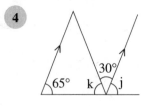
30°, 65°, k, j

5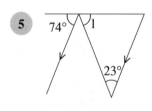
74°, l, 23°

6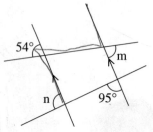
54°, m, n, 95°

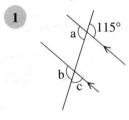

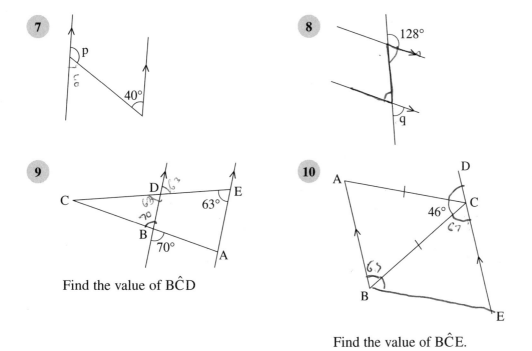

7 p 40°

8 128° q

9 C D E 63° B 70° A

Find the value of BĈD

10 A D 46° C B E

Find the value of BĈE.

HWK 5E ————————————————————— **Main Book page 106**

Find the angles marked with letters.

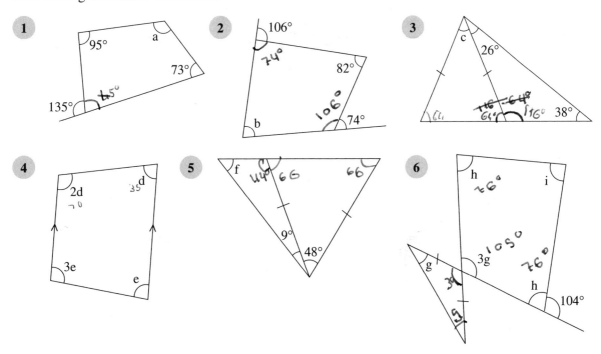

1 95° a 73° 135°

2 106° 82° b 74°

3 c 26° 38°

4 2d d 3e e

5 f 9° 48°

6 h i 3g h 104° g

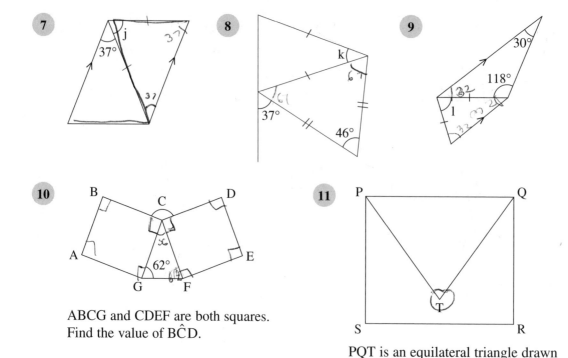

7 j, 37°, 37

8 k, 37°, 46°

9 30°, 118°

10
ABCG and CDEF are both squares.
Find the value of BĈD.

11
PQT is an equilateral triangle drawn inside the square PQRS. Find the Value of SТ̂R.

2.5 Rules of Algebra

HWK 1M ——————————————————————— **Main Book page 109**

In questions **1** to **6** write down the expression obtained.

1 I start with a number m, double it then add 6.

2 I start with a number p, multiply it by 5 then take away 3.

3 I start with a number w, multiply it by 9 then add 15.

4 I start with a number B then divide it by 4.

5 I start with a number A, multiply it by 7 then subtract 2.

6 I start with a number y, divide it by 10 then add 3.

7 Use algebra to write down the length of this piece of string.

m 3 n p

8 Fatima has *n* sweets. Her brother gives her 16 sweets. How many sweets does she now have?

9 A boy cycles *b* km and then another *c* km. How far does he cycle altogether?

10 Sandra has 38 marbles but loses *x* of them. How many marbles does Sandra now have?

11 A piece of cloth is *m* cm long. Jim cuts off *n* cm. How long is the piece of cloth now?

12 Write down an expression for the perimeter of each shape.

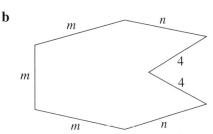

a **b**

HWK 1E ——————————————————————————— **Main Book page 111**

In questions **1** to **5** write down the expression obtained.

1 I start with *m*, double it then add *p*.

2 I start with 2*a*, add 7 then add another *b*.

3 I subtract *y* from 4*w* and then add 7*p*.

4 I add together 3*f*, 2*g* and 6*h* then subtract 9.

5 I subtract 8*b* from 4*a* and then subtract another 3*c*.

6 A bottle of water contains 2 litres. How many litres of water are contained in *w* bottles?

7 Josh has 89 pence. His sister lends him *x* pence and he spends *m* pence. How much money does he now have?

8 ⟵——— *y* cm ———⟶ Nick eats 5 cm off one end of this piece of rock. How long is the piece of rock that is left?

9 Terry has three times as many socks as Jack plus an extra 6 socks. If Jack has *n* socks, how many socks does Terry have?

10 A pizza slice costs 85p and a bottle of water costs 65p. Write down an expression for the total cost in pence of:

a *x* pizza slices and *y* bottles of water
b *m* pizza slices and 3 bottles of water
c 2*n* pizza slices and *w* bottles of water

11 A small bag of mints contains w mints. A large bag contains 4 times as many mints. Jo buys a large bag and eats 5 mints. How many mints are left in the bag?

12 A machine makes n spoons every hour. It runs for 2 hours after which w of the spoons are rejected. How many good spoons did the machine make in the 2 hours?

13 Christie earns £x per week. She is given a pay rise of £8 per week. How much will she now earn in 6 weeks?

14 Invent a question which will give the answer $3n - 7$.

HWK 2M	Main Book page 112

Simplify the following expressions where possible.

1 $6b + 2b$ **2** $7x - 3x$ **3** $9a - 4b$ **4** $5m + m$

5 $7a + 3a$ **6** $6h - 2h$ **7** $8y - 7y$ **8** $4x + 7$

9 $8m + 1$ **10** $12x + 5x$ **11** $9p - 5$ **12** $13y + y$

13 $19b - 14b$ **14** $16m + 18m$ **15** $19a - a$ **16** $19a - 3$

17 $23n - 14n$ **18** $25n + 14$ **19** $5y + 2$ **20** $6q + 22q$

HWK 2E	Main Book page 113

Simplify the following expressions as far as possible by collecting like terms.

1 $4m + 6n + 4m + 3n$ **2** $5p + 7q + 3p + 9q$ **3** $6a + 5b - 2a + 4b$

4 $8x + 12y - 6x - 9y$ **5** $16f + 19g + 6f - 12g$ **6** $7m + 9 + m - 6$

7 $2b + 6c + 5b - 4c$ **8** $9m + 8 - 2m - 7$ **9** $15 + 4y + 12 - 3y$

10 $6x + 15y - 10y + x$ **11** $4a + 23 + 7 - 2a$ **12** $11 + 5n - 7 + 2n$

13 $12w - 3w + 8 + 7$ **14** $13p + 19 - 9p - 2p$ **15** $16 + 12m - 3 + 12$

16 $6a + 4b - 2b + 9$ **17** $8n + 3 - 7n + 4p$ **18** $7x + 5y + 6 - x$

In questions **19** to **21**, copy and complete the number chains.

19 $\boxed{3a} \xrightarrow{+} \boxed{5b} = \boxed{} \xrightarrow{+} \boxed{7b} = \boxed{} \xrightarrow{-} \boxed{2a} = \boxed{} \xrightarrow{+} \boxed{9a} = \boxed{}$

20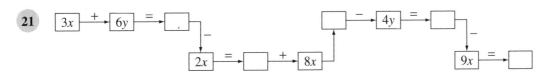

$7m$ → $+$ → 9 → $=$ → ☐ → $+$
16 → $=$ → ☐ → $+$ → $5m$ → ☐ → $-$
$10m$ → $=$ → ☐ → $-$ → 25 → $=$ → ☐

21

$3x$ → $+$ → $6y$ → $=$ → ☐ → $-$
☐ → $-$ → $4y$ → $=$ → ☐ → $-$
$2x$ → $=$ → ☐ → $+$ → $8x$
$9x$ → $=$ → ☐

22 $16m + 9n +$ ☐ $= 19m + 5n$ What belongs in the empty box?

23 $12x + 6y +$ ☐ $= y$ What belongs in the empty box?

| **HWK 3M** | **Main Book page 114** |

1   List the expressions below which are equal to $3n$.

| $3 + n$ | $3 \times n$ | $n + n + n$ | $3 \div n$ |

| $4n - n$ | $3 - n$ | $2n + n$ | $n \times 3$ |

2   **a** Write down any pairs of expressions from below that are equal to each other.

| $6 - n$ | $4n + n$ | $\dfrac{3}{n}$ | $n + n$ |

| $5 \times n$ | $\dfrac{n}{3}$ | $7n - 5n$ | $n - 6$ |

   b For each chosen pair from part **a**, write down a value for n which shows that you are correct.

3   **a** List the expressions below which are equal to $2a + 3b$.

| $a + a + b + b$ | $5a + 3b - 3$ | $3a + 3b - a$ | $2a + 2b + b$ |

| $6a + b - 4a + 2b$ | $a + 4b - b + a$ | $2a + 2b + 1$ | $7a + 6b - 5a - 2b$ |

   b For each expression you have chosen, use $a = 5$ and $b = 4$ to check that each one is equal to the value of $2a + 3b$.

In questions **4** to **18** write down each statement and say whether it is 'true' or 'false'.

4 $4 \times m = 4m$

5 $x + x + x + x = 4x$

6 $n + 5 = 5 + n$

7 $a \times a = a^2$

8 $10 + w = 10w$

9 $8 - n = n - 8$

10 $mn = nm$

11 $b \div 4 = 4 \div b$

12 $2 \times p = p^2$

13 $x + y + x = 2x + y$

14 $m + n + p = mnp$

15 $\dfrac{a}{3} = \dfrac{3}{a}$

16 $5n - n = 5$

17 $w \times 9 = 9w$

18 $3y + 5 = 8y$

HWK 3E | **Main Book page 115**

Simplify

1 $6m \times 3n$

2 $9p \times 4q$

3 $5y \times 5w$

4 $8a \times b$

5 $7m \times 3n \times 2p$

6 $4p \times 2 \times 5q$

7 $5m \times 6 \times 3n$

8 $9 \times 5a \times c$

9 $(4n)^2$

10 Simplify by collecting like terms

a $4ab - ba$

b $6xy + 3pq - pq + 2yx$

c $5w + 3p + pw - 4w$

d $5mn + 7n - 3nm + 2 - 5n$

e $9a + 2ab + a - ba - 4a$

f $6y + 3yx - 3y + 2xy - y$

g $8c + 3 - 2c + 4cd - dc$

h $5ab + 6a - ba + 3ab + 3$

11 Find an expression for the total area of these four rectangles.

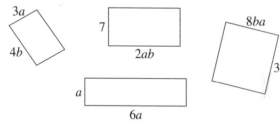

12 Phil has $3mn$ sweets. He eats nm sweets then Alice gives him $2pq$ sweets. Phil now eats $(mn + qp)$ sweets. How many sweets has he got left now?

13 Josie is $(5ab + 7b)$ metres tall. Jack is $(4ba + b)$ metres tall. How much taller is Josie than Jack? (we are assuming that Josie is taller)

14

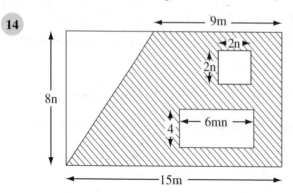

Find an expression for the shaded area.

1 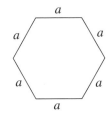 The perimeter p of this hexagon is given by the formula $p = 6a$.
Find p when $a = 4$.

2 The perimeter p of a rectangle with sides m and n is given by the formula $p = 2m + 2n$.
Find p when $m = 7$ and $n = 3$.

3 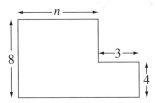 The area A of this shape is given by the formula $A = 8n + 12$.

Find A when   **a** $n = 3$ **b** $n = 10$ **c** $n = 27$

4 The perimeter p of a shape is given by the formula $p = 5n + 17m$. Find p when $n = 8$ and $m = 6$.

5 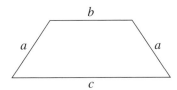 A formula for the perimeter p of this trapezium is

$p = 2a + b + c$

Find p when $a = 12$, $b = 19$ and $c = 33$.

6 The area A of a shape is given by the formula

$A = xy + 7m$

Find A when   **a** $x = 3$, $y = 6$ and $m = 5$

                     b $x = 7$, $y = 11$ and $m = 15$

                     c $x = 0.5$, $y = 0.3$ and $m = 0.2$

A formula is given in each question. Find the value of the letter required in each case.

1 $m = 2n + 9$ Find m when $n = 6$ **2** $b = 2c - 5$ Find b when $c = 8$

3 $a = 23 - b$ Find a when $b = 16$ **4** $w = 33 - 4y$ Find w when $y = 5$

5 $f = \dfrac{h}{8}$ Find f when $h = 56$ **6** $y = 5(x + 3)$ Find y when $x = 6$

7 $a = bc$ Find a when $b = 3$, $c = 12$ **8** $k = \dfrac{m}{9} + 13$ Find k when $m = 72$

9 $p = 7(28 - q)$ Find p when $q = 19$

10 $y = x(x - 4)$ Find y when $x = 15$

11 $m = 8np$ Find m when $n = 2, p = 6$

12 $a = b^2$ Find a when $b = 12$

13 $d = \dfrac{e}{7} - 6$ Find d when $e = 49$

14 $v = w(w + y)$ Find v when $w = 8, y = 5$

15 $y = xw - x$ Find y when $x = 11, w = 4$

16 $m = n^2 + p^2 - t^2$
Find m when $n = 6, p = 20, t = 8$

17 $c = \dfrac{5d + 3}{11}$ Find c when $d = 6$

18 $y = x^2(x^2 + 4)$ Find y when $x = 6$

19 $m = \dfrac{n(2n - p)}{2p}$
Find m when $n = 10, p = 5$

20 $a = \dfrac{b^2 + 4b}{3c}$
Find a when $b = 6, c = 4$

HWK 5M	**Main Book page 119**

Find the value of the required symbol.

1   Find ∇ if $\star$ = 18.

2   Find ∇ if $\frown$ = 15.

3   Find $\star$ if $\frown$ = 12.

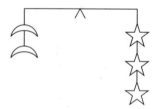

4   Find $\frown$ if ∇ = 20.

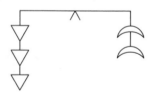

5   Find $\frown$ if $\star$ = 18.

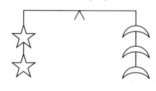

6   Find $\star$ if ∇ = 9.

7   Find ∇ if $\frown$ = 30.

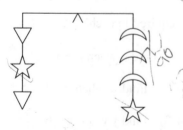

8   Find $\frown$ if $\star$ = 10.

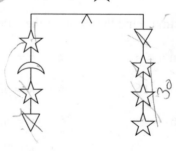

9   Find $\star$ if $\frown$ = 9.

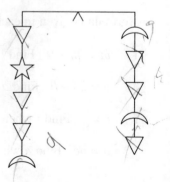

Find the value of the required symbol.

1 Find ⌒ and ▽ if ☆ = 18.

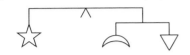

2 Find ⌒ and ☆ if ▽ = 28.

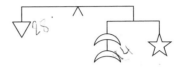

3 Find ▽ and ⌒ if ☆ = 12.

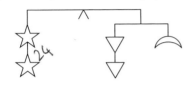

4 Find ▽ and ☆ if ⌒ = 10.

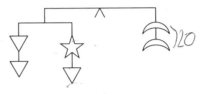

5 Find ☆ and ⌒ if ▽ = 6.

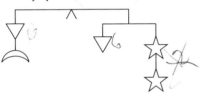

6 Find ⌒ and ☆ if ▽ = 8.

7 Find ☆ and ▽ if ⌒ = 14.

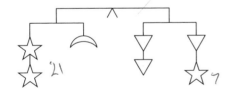

8 Find ☆ and ▽ if ⌒ = 12.

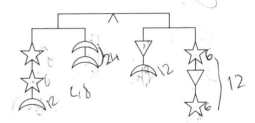

9 Find ☆ and ⌒ if ▽ = 20.

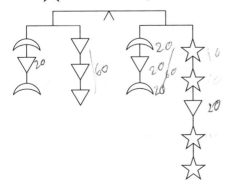

10 Find ⌒ and ▽ if ☆ = 30.

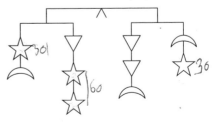

UNIT 3

3.1 Coordinates

The letters from A to Z are shown on the grid. Coded messages can be sent using coordinates.

For example (–4, –2) (–4, 2) (–4, 2) (4, 2) reads 'FOOD'.

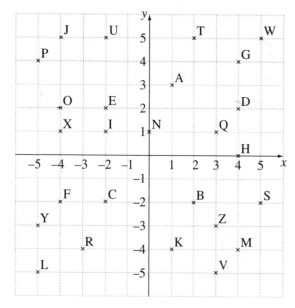

Decipher the following messages

1 (5, 5) (4, 0) (1, 3) (2, 5) # (4, 2) (–4, 2) # (–5, –3)
(–4, 2) (–2, 5) # (–2, –2) (1, 3) (–5, –5) (–5, –5) #
(1, 3) # (4, –4) (1, 3) (0, 1) # (5, 5) (–2, 1) (2, 5) (4, 0) #
(1, 3) # (5, –2) (–5, 4) (1, 3) (4, 2) (–2, 2) # (–2, 1)
(0, 1) # (4, 0) (–2, 1) (5, –2) # (4, 0) (–2, 2) (1, 3)
(4, 2)? # (4, 2) (–4, 2) (–2, 5) (4, 4) !

2 (5, 5) (4, 0) (1, 3) (2, 5) # (4, 2) (–4, 2) # (–5, –3)
(–4, 2) (–2, 5) # (–2, –2) (1, 3) (–5, –5) (–5, –5) #
(1, 3) # (4, 2) (–2, 2) (1, 3) (4, 2) # (–5, 4) (1, 3) (–3, –4)
(–3, –4) (–4, 2) (2, 5) ? # (–5, 4) (–4, 2) (–5, –5) (–5, –3)
(4, 4) (–4, 2) (0, 1) !

3   (5, 5) (–2, 1) (2, 5) (4, 0) # (5, 5) (4, 0) (1, 3) (2, 5) #

(4, 2) (–4, 2) # (–5, –3) (–4, 2) (–2, 5) # (5, –2) (2, 5)

(–2, 5) (–4, –2) (–4, –2) # (1, 3) # (4, 2) (–2, 2) (1, 3)

(4, 2) # (–5, 4) (1, 3) (–3, –4) (–3, –4) (–4, 2)

(2, 5) ? # (–5, 4) (–4, 2) (–5, –5) (–5, –3) (–4, –2) (–2, 1)

(–5, –5) (–5, –5) (1, 3) !

4   Write a message or joke of your own using co-ordinates. Ask a friend to decipher your words at the start of your next lesson.

| **HWK 2M** | **Main Book page 136** |

Plot the points given and join them up in order. Write down what the picture is.

1   Draw the x axis (horizontal axis) from 0 to 16 and the y axis (vertical axis) from 0 to 10.

  a (12, 2), (13, 2), (12, 4)

  b (6, 2), (7, 2), (7, 5), (11, 4), (11, 1), (12, 1), (12, 4),✓
     (13, $5\frac{1}{2}$), (15$\frac{1}{2}$, 5$\frac{1}{2}$), (15$\frac{1}{2}$, 8), (15, 8), (15, 6), (13, 6),✓
     (12, 7), (6, 8), (6, 9), (5, 10), (5, 9), (2, 8), (2, 7),✓
     (3, 7), (2, 6), (5, 7), (5, 1), (6, 1), (6, 4), (7, 5). ✓

  c Draw a dot at (4, 8).

2   Draw the x axis (horizontal axis) from 0 to 14 and the y axis (vertical axis) from 0 to 10.

  a (5, 5), (5, 6), (11, 6), (11, 5)✓

  b (7, 6), (7, 7), (8, 7), (8, 6)✓

  c ($5\frac{1}{2}$, 7), ($5\frac{1}{2}$, 8), (4, 8), (4, 9)

  d (5, 6), (5, 7), (6, 7), (6, 6)

  e ($7\frac{1}{2}$, 7), ($7\frac{1}{2}$, 8), (6, 8), (6, 9)

3   Draw the x axis from 0 to 18 and the y axis from 0 to 9.

  a Plot the following points and join them up in order
     (1, 2), (3, 3), (6, 3), (6, 2), (4, 1), (1, 1), (1, 2), (4, 2), (4, 1), (4, 2), (6, 3)

  b Multiply all the coordinates by 3, plot the new points and join them up to draw a new picture.

  c For each of the original points add 10 to the x coordinate and keep the same y coordinate. For example, (1, 2) becomes (11, 2) and (3, 3) becomes (13, 3). Plot the new points and join them up.

  d Look at the solid you drew in part (a). How many of these would be needed to fill completely the solid drawn in part (b)?

60

1   **a** T, R and S are three corners of a square.
        Write down the co-ordinates of the other
        corner.

   b R, S and U are three corners
        of a rectangle. Write down the
        co-ordinates of the other corner.

   c P, Q and R are three corners of another
        square. Write down the co-ordinates of
        the other corner. (Draw the diagram if
        you need to)

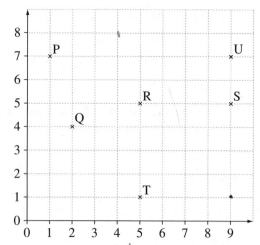

2   Draw a grid with values from 0 to 7. Plot the three points given and then find the co-ordinates
     of the point which makes a parallelogram when the points are joined up.

     (4, 1)   (2, 3)   (2, 7)

3   A trapezium has one   A kite has two pairs
     pair of parallel sides.   of adjacent equal sides.

The graph shows three incomplete shapes.
Copy the diagram and show two possible
positions for the fourth vertex (corner) of
each shape.
Write down the coordinates of the points
you find.

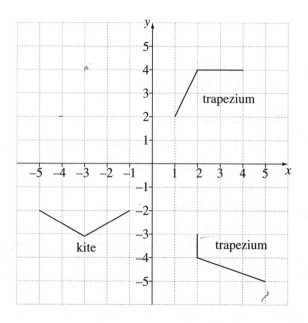

4 **a** Draw a pair of axes with values of *x* and *y* from 0 to 10.

  b A(7, 2), B(1, 3) and C(4, 6) are three vertices (corners) of a parallelogram. Draw and complete the parallelogram ABCD.

  c Draw a line from A which is perpendicular to AD and meets the *y* axis. Write down the coordinates of the point E where this line meets the *y* axis.

  d Draw a vertical line from B which intersects line AE at F.

  e Label a point G which is one third of the way along line BC starting from B.

  f Draw a line from G which is perpendicular to BC and meets the line BF at H. Write down the length of FH.

3.2 Long multiplication and division 2

HWK 1M/1E	Main Book page 140

1 Use any method to work out

  a 46 × 37   **b** 69 × 69   **c** 425 × 28   **d** 372 × 43

2 Work out (there may be remainders)

  a 702 ÷ 27   **b** 637 ÷ 34   **c** 519 ÷ 24   **d** 473 ÷ 28

3 74 students each have to sit 13 exams. How many exams is this in total?

4 There are 217 people on a ship. The ship hits an iceberg and starts to sink. Each lifeboat can take 18 people. How many lifeboats are needed to get everyone safely off the ship?

5 Lauren spends £119 on each day of her 14 day holiday. How much does she spend in total?

6 Find the missing number.

  a ☐ × 19 = 1026   **b** 43 × ☐ = 1204   **c** ☐ ÷ 48 = 37   **d** 2772 ÷ ☐ = 44

7 Simon's heart beats 81 times each minute. How many times will his heart beat in a quarter of an hour?

8 John sells 38 computer games at £46 each and 73 dvds at £13 each. Marcia sells 56 dvds at £12 each and 45 computer games at £45 each. Who takes most money?

3.3 Decimals 2

HWK 1M	Main Book page 143

Work out

1 9 − 6.8   **2** 0.3 + 5 + 2.14   **3** 0.718 × 10   **4** 16.4 − 11.7

5 $312 \div 100$ **6** 0.9×0.03 **7** $5.4 - 2.16$ **8** $3.6 \div 5$

9 5.8×200 **10** $19 - 5.82$ **11** $14.52 \div 3$ **12** 0.6×1.2

13 $17.6 + 3.82 + 4$ **14** 0.08×1000 **15** 0.2×0.008 **16** $1.841 \div 7$

17 Eight fence panels are used to fence a length of 14 m. How long is each fence panel?

18 Find the missing number.

a $\Box + 1.87 = 12$ **b** $\Box - 0.58 = 7.6$ **c** $\Box \div 9 = 2.46$

d $4 \times \Box = 13.12$ **e** $\Box \div 4 = 7.39$ **f** $2.9 - \Box = 1.17$

g $\Box \times 7 = 46.2$ **h** $100 \times \Box = 98.2$ **i** $\Box \div 5 = 4.3$

HWK 1E   **Main Book page 143**

1 Find the total cost of 6 pineapples at £1.84 each.

2 A sheet of metal weighing 51.2 kg is to be divided into 8 equal parts. How much will each part weigh?

3 10.7 litres of paint are poured equally into 5 tins. How much paint is in each tin?

4 Copy and complete

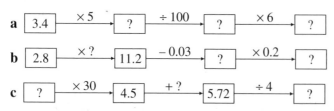

5 The perimeter of a square is 14.4 m. Find the area of the square.

6 Six friends have a meal in a restaurant which costs £108.19. Sandra pays £24.69 and each of the other five people pay an equal amount. How much do each of the other people pay?

7 Ben can buy six books for £27.60. How many books can he buy for £50.60?

8 Find the missing numbers

a $23 - (30.1 \div \Box) = 18.7$ **b** $14.86 + (0.4 \times \Box) = 15.18$

9 During one week Helen drinks the following amount of water in litres each day: 1.42, 2, 0.97, 1.23, 1.81, 1.46 and 1.12. Find her mean average daily amount of water.

10 Anna makes 1kg of fudge which costs her £3.40. She sells the fudge at 45p for every 50 g. How much profit does she make if she sells all the fudge?

HWK 2M

Main Book page 144

Draw a copy of the crossnumber puzzle and then fill it in using the clues given.

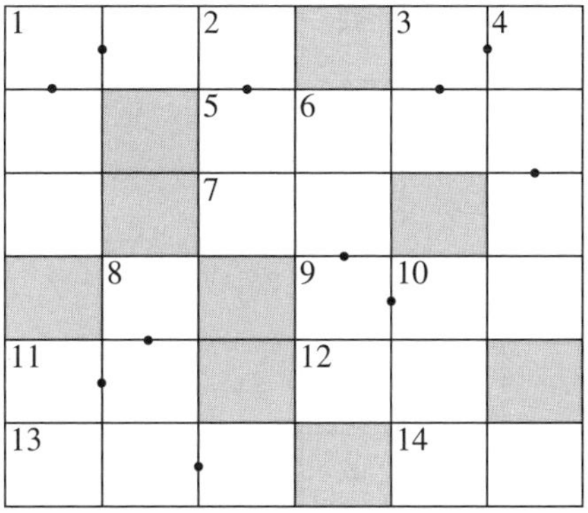

Clues across

1. 19 × 0.04
3. 740 ÷ 200
5. (3.714 + 3.48) × 1000
7. 0.9^2 × 100 + 1
9. 0.8^2 × 10 – 0.08
11. 9.46 – 1.56
12. (0.0086 × 100) × 100
13. 132 ÷ 8
14. 7 × 12 – (0.02 × 800)

Clues down

1. 1.6 – 0.97
2. 2.1^2 + 2.37
3. 27.3 ÷ 7
4. 934 × 0.08
6. 50.72 ÷ 4
8. 7.73 – 1.77
10. 1.22 × 300
11. (5.64 + 3.9 – 2.44) × 10

HWK 2E

Main Book page 145

Each empty square contains either a number or an operation (+ , –, ×, ÷). Copy each square and fill in the missing details. The arrows are equals signs.

1

0.15	×	7	→	
×				
	×	3.8	→	
↓		↓		
15	+	3.2	→	

2

4.7	÷		→	0.47
–		×		
0.84	+		→	0.92
↓		↓		
	–		→	

3

12.6		100	→	0.126
÷				
5	×	1.9	→	
↓		↓		
	+	190	→	

4

8.16	×	100	→	
×				
20		25	→	500
↓		↓		
	÷	4	→	

5

9.4	×	8	→	
+		–		
	+		→	
↓		↓		
12.36	–		→	8.63

6

	×	0.16	→	
÷		÷		
2		2	→	4
↓		↓		↓
0.1	×		→	

3.4 Properties of numbers

HWK 1M/1E ——————————————————— **Main Book page 47**

1 Write down all the prime numbers shown below.

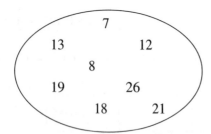

2 When two prime numbers are added the answer is 18. What could the two numbers be?

3 The difference between 2 prime numbers is another prime number. Write down 3 sets of numbers where this would be true.

4 Write down all the prime numbers between 30 and 40.

5 Is 89 a prime number?

6 How many prime numbers are there between 60 and 70?

7 **a** List all the prime numbers between 100 and 110.
b Explain what you did to check that these numbers were prime.

8 | 371 | | 285 | | 509 | Find out which of these numbers are prime.

| 994 | | 627 | | 483 |

9 Find four prime numbers which add up to another prime number.

HWK 2M ———————————————————— **Main Book page 149**

1 Write down all the factors of   **a** 8   **b** 22   **c** 30

2 How many factors does 28 have?

3 The factors of a number are 1, 5 and 25. What is the number?

4 The number in each circle is the product of the numbers in the squares on either side. Find the missing numbers.

a 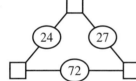   **b** 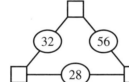   **c**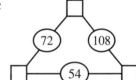

5 How many numbers less than 10 have exactly 2 factors?

6 How many factors does each prime number have?

7 Write down all the *odd* factors of 60.

HWK 2E ———————————————————— **Main Book page 150**

1 Here is a factor tree for 45

```
        45
       /  \
      9    5
     / \
    3   3
```

45 = 3 × 3 × 5

a branch ends when you get a prime number

a Draw a factor tree for 40.
b Copy and complete
40 = ? × ? × ? × ?

66

2 **a** Draw a factor tree for 48.

      b Copy and complete 48 = ? × ? × ? × ? × ?

3 Draw a factor tree for each number below and write down the prime factors.

      a 120   **b** 300   **c** 350   **d** 365   **e** 3185

4 Write down a four-digit number which has 7 and 13 as factors

5 How many different prime factors does 405 have?

6 What is the smallest whole number which is exactly divisible by all the numbers from 1 to 12 inclusive?

HWK 3M ──────────────────────────────── **Main Book page 151**

1 Write down the first five multiples of 18.

2 Which numbers below are *not* multiples of 15?

| 30 | 70 | 60 | 90 | 80 | 45 |

3 Which numbers below are multiples of 7?

| 28 | 63 | 36 | 82 | 84 | 54 |

4 Find three numbers that are multiples of both 4 and 5.

5 Find two numbers that are multiples of 3, 4 and 8.

6 **a** Which of the numbers below is not a multiple of 21?

      b Which of the numbers below is a factor of 126?

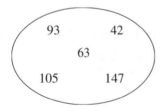

93   42
    63
105   147

7 Find the lowest number which is a multiple of 4, 6 and 8.

HWK 3E ——————————————————————— **Main Book page 152**

1 The factors of 18 are 1, 2, 3, 6, 9, 18.

The factors of 12 are 1, 2, 3, 4, 6, 12.

Write down the <u>H</u>ighest <u>C</u>ommon <u>F</u>actor of 18 and 12.

2 **a** List all the factors of 20.

b List all the factors of 30.

c Write down the HCF of 20 and 30.

3 Find the HCF of

a 24 and 36 **b** 57 and 95 **c** 25, 45 and 60

4 9, 18, 27, 36, 45 are multiples of 9.

12, 24, 36, 48, 60 are multiples of 12.

Write down the <u>L</u>owest <u>C</u>ommon <u>M</u>ultiple of 9 and 12.

5 **a** List the first 6 multiples of 6.

b List the first 6 multiples of 8.

c Write down the LCM of 6 and 8.

6 Find the LCM of

a 4 and 9 **b** 12 and 15 **c** 5, 7 and 11

7 Write down two numbers whose LCM is 20.

8 Find the HCF of 42 and 56.

9 If $228 = 2 \times 2 \times 3 \times 19$ and $285 = 3 \times 5 \times 19$, find the highest common factor of 228 and 285.

10 If $2730 = 2 \times 3 \times 5 \times 7 \times 13$ and $63063 = 3 \times 3 \times 7 \times 7 \times 11 \times 13$, find the highest common factor of 2730 and 63063.

HWK 4M/4E ——————————————————————— **Main Book page 154**

Work out

1 9^2 **2** 11^2 **3** $5^2 + 3^2$ **4** $10^2 - 6^2$

5 $12^2 + 8^2$ **6** $20^2 - 10^2$ **7** $13^2 + 11^2$ **8** $13^2 \times 17^2$

9 $7^2 + 15^2 - 14^2$ **10** $(5^2 - 3^2)^2$ **11** Answer true or false 'The number of squares on a chessboard is a square number.'

12 Find a pair of square numbers with a difference of:

    a 51　　　　　**b** 55　　　　　　**c** 77　　　　　　**d** 96

13 Use a calculator to find out which number, when multiplied by itself, gives a product of:

    a 2116　　　　**b** 784　　　　　**c** 1024　　　　**d** 6889

14 Which of these numbers are *not* cube numbers?

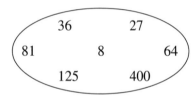

15 **a** Copy and complete the pattern below as far as 10 × 10.

        $2 \times 2 = 1 \times 1 + 3$

        $3 \times 3 = 2 \times 2 + 5$

        $4 \times 4 = 3 \times 3 + 7$

        $5 \times 5 = 4 \times 4 + ..$

        $\vdots$

        $10 \times 10 = ...$

    b What is the result for 15 × 15?

    c What is the result for 20 × 20?

16 Work out

    a $\sqrt{81} - \sqrt{36}$　　　　**b** $\sqrt{196} + \sqrt{1}$　　　　**c** $\sqrt{(4^2 + \sqrt{81})}$

17 Write 68 as a product of its prime factors. What is the smallest number by which you can multiply 68 so that the answer is a square number?

3.5 Straight line graphs

1

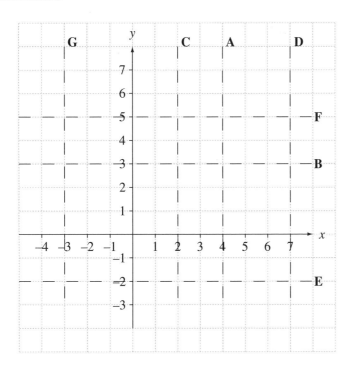

The equation of line A is $x = 4$

The equation of line B is $y = 3$

Write down the equations of the lines C, D, E, F and G.

2 Draw x and y axes from 0 to 6. Draw the lines $x = 5$ and $y = 1$ and write down the coordinates of the point where the two lines meet.

3 Draw x and y axes from 0 to 6.

Plot and label the points P (2, 1), Q (4, 4), R (6, 2), S (5, 2), T (6, 4), U (2, 6) and V (2, 4). S and R lie on the line $y = 2$.

a List the points on the line $y = 4$.

b Write down the equation of the line passing through R and T.

c List the points on the line $x = 2$.

d List the points on the line $x = 5$.

e List the points with the sum of x and y equal to 8.

f List the points with the sum of x and y equal to a prime number.

70

1 For each graph write down the coordinates of the points marked and find the equation of the line through the points.

a

b

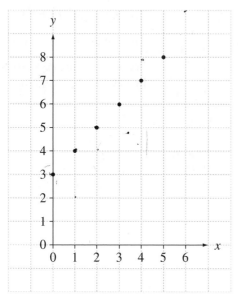
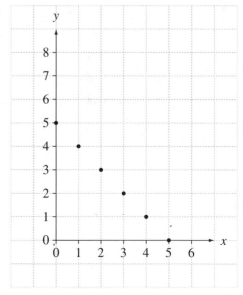

2 Write down the equation of the line which passes through the points (1, 2), (2, 4), (3, 6), (4, 8) and (5, 10).

3

x	y
10	4
11	5
12	6
13	7

This table shows some points on a line.

Find the equation of the line.

4 Find the equation for

a line A   **b** line B

c line C   **d** line D

e This is the table for the points on line E

x	10	11	12	13	14
y	0	2	4	6	8

Find the equation of line E.

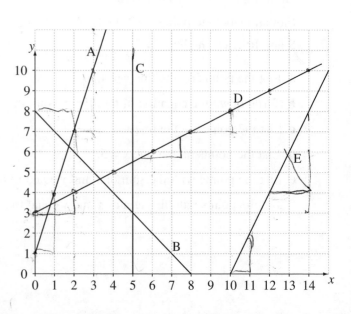

HWK 2M ————————————————————————— **Main Book page 163**

1 For the line $y = x - 5$, find the y values for

    a $x = 8$ **b** $x = 10$ **c** $x = 11$

2 For the line $y = 6x$, find the y values for

    a $x = 3$ **b** $x = 7$ **c** $x = 12$

3 Does the point $(3, 12)$ lie on the line $y = 4x$ or on the line $y = 9x$?

4 Which points below lie on the line $y = 7 - x$?

    A$(2, 9)$ B$(3, 4)$ C$(1, 6)$ D$(3, 10)$

5 Consider the two lines: $y = 3x + 2$ and $y = 2x - 1$. State which of the points below lie on each line.

    P$(4, 7)$ Q$(0, -1)$ R$(2, 8)$ S$(5, 9)$ T$(7, 23)$

6

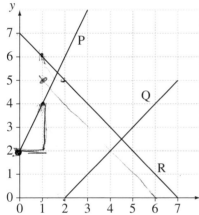

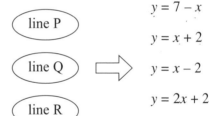

$y = 7 - x$

$y = x + 2$

$y = x - 2$

$y = 2x + 2$

$y = 2x - 2$

Match up lines P, Q and R to the correct equation.

7 Write down any 3 points which lie on the line $y = 4x + 1$.

HWK 2E ————————————————————————— **Main Book page 164**

Fill in the missing numbers for each equation. Draw x and y axes then draw the graph.

1 $y = x - 3$; $(0, -3)$ $(1, -2)$ $(2, \square)$ $(3, \square)$ $(4, \square)$

2 $y = 5 - x$; $(0, \square)$ $(1, \square)$ $(2, \square)$ $(3, \square)$

3 $y = 2x - 1;$ (1, 1)   (2, ☐)   (3, ☐)   (4, ☐)   (5, ☐)

4 $y = 4 - 2x;$ (0, ☐)   (1, 2)   (2, ☐)   (3, ☐)

5   **a** Draw x and y axes each with values from 0 to 6.

     b Draw the lines $y = 2x + 1$ and $y = 4 - x$ on the same graph.

     c Write down the coordinates of the point where the lines meet.

3.6 Handling data

HWK 1M/1E	Main Book page 165

1 Some children were asked how many times they had a drink of water each day. The replies are listed below:

     2   4   3   0   2   4   6   5

     5   2   7   1   3   3   2   6

     1   3   6   4   5   1   0   3

     6   3   4   4   2   5   3   4

     a Copy and complete the frequency table.

     b Draw a bar chart to show the results.

number of times	tally	frequency
0		
1		
2		
3		
4		
5		
6		
7		

2   **a** Ask as many people as you can to tell you how many portions of fruit and vegetables they eat on an average day.

     b Use the results to make a frequency table.

     c Draw a bar chart to show the results.

     d What are the most portions eaten?

     e What are the least portions eaten?

     f Do you think these people eat enough fruit and vegetables? **Explain** why you think this.

1 Here is a frequency diagram showing how many children there are in several primary schools.

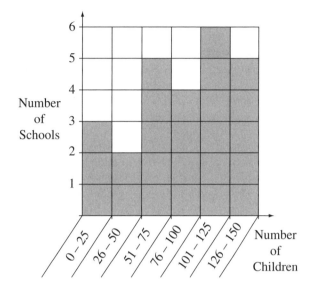

   a How many schools have between 101 and 125 children?

   b How many schools have between 51 and 100 children?

   c How many schools are there altogether?

   d How many schools have less than 76 children?

2 Some children collect Warhammer pieces. 24 children were asked how many pieces they have. The findings are shown below.

| 38 | 12 | 63 | 18 | 42 | 87 | 56 | 55 | 72 | 8 | 19 | 26 |
| 82 | 59 | 13 | 73 | 23 | 68 | 31 | 17 | 44 | 12 | 95 | 48 |

   a Put the heights into groups.

   b Draw a frequency diagram.

   c How many children had between 41 and 80 pieces?

Number of pieces	frequency
0 – 20	
21 – 40	
41 – 60	
61 – 80	
81 – 100	

3 This line graph shows the depth of water in a stream throughout the year.

   a How deep was the stream in March?

   b In which two months was the stream 8 cm deep?

   c Which month saw the largest increase in depth? Why do you think this happened?

   d What was the range of the depths?

Depth of Stream (cm)

16 14 12 10 8 6 4 2

J F M A M J J A S O N D

Months

74

4 The temperature in a centrally heated house is recorded every hour from 06:00 till 21:00. The results are shown below.

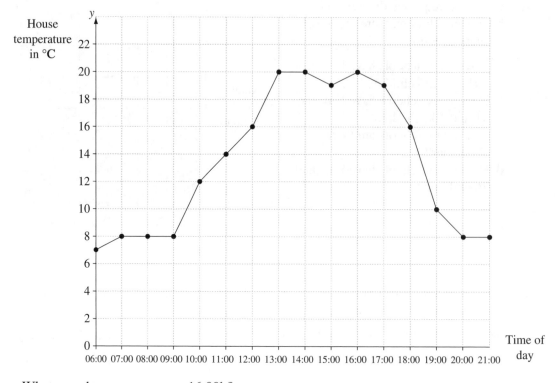

a What was the temperature at 16:00h?
b What was the temperature at 10:00h?
c What was the temperature at 12:30h?
d Write down the two times when the temperature was 16°C.
e When do you think the central heating was switched on?
f Write down the two times when the temperature was 10°C.
g When do you think the central heating was switched off?

HWK 3M ──────────────────────────── **Main Book page 174**

1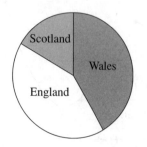

240 children attended a meeting. The pie chart shows what fraction of the children came from England, Scotland and Wales.

a *Roughly* how many children came from Scotland?
b *About* how many children came from Wales?

2 Some children were asked to state their favourite animal. The results are shown by the pie charts below.

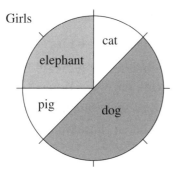

There were 80 girls.   There were 64 boys.

Anna says 'The same number of boys and girls chose elephant'.

Harry says 'More girls than boys chose elephant'.

a Use both charts to explain whether Anna is correct.

b Use both charts to explain whether Harry is correct.

3 Some people were asked what their favourite city in Europe was. The results are shown by the pie charts below.

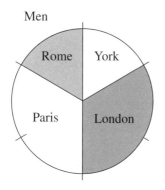 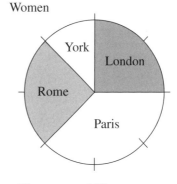

There were 180 men.   There were 120 women.

Marie says 'The same number of men and women prefer Rome'.

David says 'More women than men prefer Rome'.

a Use both charts to explain whether Marie or David is correct.

b Did more or less men than women prefer York? *Explain* your answer.

76

1

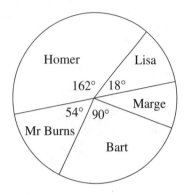

300 children were asked who their favourite Simpsons character is. This pie chart shows their answers.

a How many children chose Lisa?

b How many children chose Mr Burns?

c How many children chose Homer?

d What angle represents Marge?

e How many children chose Marge?

In questions **2** and **3** work out the angle for each sector and draw a pie chart.

2 Favourite footballer in 2008

Footballer	frequency
Ronaldo	30
Fabregas	16
Drogba	6
Torres	20

3 Amount of Exercise taken each day

Amount of Exercise	frequency
None	12
$\frac{1}{2}$ hour	13
1 hour	6
$1\frac{1}{2}$ hours	3
2 hours	4
$2\frac{1}{2}$ hours	2

4 Last Saturday there were 5 films showing at the local cinema.

38 people watched 'Conrad'

50 people watched 'Harry Potter 9'

24 people watched 'Major Joe'

88 people watched 'High Terror'

40 people watched 'Horatio'

Draw a pie chart to show this information.

3.7 Probability 1

1

impossible   unlikely   evens   likely   certain

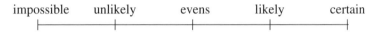

This is a probability scale. Some events are listed below. Write down which events are shown in the correct place on the probability scale above.

a You will get married next week.

b You will have a birthday in the next year.

c Your teacher will win the Lottery and retire to the Bahamas.

d When a coin is tossed it will show 'tails'.

e The sun will rise tomorrow.

f In the next TV series, Doctor Who will defeat the aliens and save the planet!

2 Draw this probability scale.

impossible   unlikely   evens   likely   certain

Draw an arrow to show the chance of the events below happening.

a A baby will be born somewhere in the world today.

b The next match a football team play will be a home game.

c Next time you roll a dice, you will get an even number.

d You will grow an extra leg tonight then win the next Olympics 100 m race.

e You will get at least one birthday card when you have your next birthday.

f You will see your headteacher before you get to school on your next school day.

3

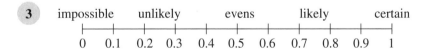

impossible   unlikely   evens   likely   certain

0   0.1   0.2   0.3   0.4   0.5   0.6   0.7   0.8   0.9   1

Look at the events in questions **1** and **2** and for each one estimate the probability of it occurring using a probability from 0 to 1. (for example: question **2** **b** might be 'about 0.5')

4 Think of 4 events and show where they would be on the probability scale.

In your next lesson ask another person if they agree with where you have shown your events.

HWK 2M ———————————————————————— **Main Book page 182**

1 Get a shoe.

2 Spin the shoe in the air and see if it lands 'the right way up', ie. the heel on the bottom.

3 You must do this 50 times. Each time is called a 'trial' and you must record each time the shoe lands the 'right way up' (a 'success').

A tally chart like below may help.

Number of trials	Number of successes
ЖГ III	III

4 Use a calculator to work out the experimental probability that a shoe will land the 'right way up' when it is thrown in the air.

Reminder:

$$\text{experimental probability} = \frac{\text{number of successes}}{\text{total number of trials}}$$

HWK 3M/3E ———————————————————————— **Main Book page 183**

1 What is the probability that each spinner will land on a shaded part?

a    b   c   d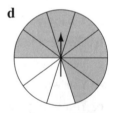

2    These 7 balls are mixed up in a bag. Rosa picks out one ball. What is the probability that she picks:

a   b (★)   c (▲)

3 8 football clubs are in the draw for the quarter–finals of the F.A. Cup.

Arsenal	Liverpool
Newcastle Utd	West Ham Utd
Everton	Chelsea
Manchester Utd	Manchester City

What is the probability that the first club to be chosen will be West Ham?

4 There are ten identical beads in a bag.

(B) (B) (B) (B) (B)
(W) (W) (W) (T) (T)

I take out one bead.
Work out the probability of taking out:

a (W) **b** (B) **c** (T)

5 I roll an ordinary dice. Find the probability that it lands on

a 4 **b** 2 **c** more than 3

6 There are 20 beads in a bag. 10 beads are blue, 3 beads are red, 2 beads are green and 5 beads are yellow.

I take out one bead.
Find the probability of:

a taking out a red bead.

b taking out a blue bead.

c taking out a yellow bead.

d taking out a green bead.

e taking out a blue or red bead.

f taking out a black bead.

7 There are 25 identical fish in a tank. 8 fish are gold. 12 fish are red.

The rest of the fish are yellow. I catch one fish. Find the probability of:

a catching a red fish.

b catching a gold fish.

c catching a yellow or red fish.

d catching a gold, yellow or red fish.

8 Using this spinner, what is the probability of getting:

a the number 7 **b** an even number

c a multiple of 4 **d** a prime number

e a factor of 56 **f** a cube number

9

| C | A | N | T | A | N | K | E | R | O | U | S |

Tania shuffles these cards then picks one out. What is the probability that she picks:

a the letter N **b** a letter in the second half of the alphabet

c a letter in the word 'NOTE'

3.8 Applying mathematics in a range of contexts

1 There are 673 dogs and cats at a pet show. There are 37 more dogs than cats. How many dogs are there?

2 The perimeter of this shape is 42cm. What is the area of this shape?

3 Hilary makes and sells cards for £1.75 each. Her basic material costs £4.32 to make 12 cards. She pays £4.50 for 50 envelopes to put the cards in. She spends another 16p on materials for each card. How much profit does she make for each card she sells.

4 Every year a population of rabbits trebles and adds 1. There are 10 rabbits at the start of 2001. How many rabbits will there be at the start of 2011?

5 Write down a factor of 36 which is also a multiple of 4. Write down all the possible answers.

6 How large is angle x?

7 It costs 14p per minute to ring Perth in Australia. How much will a phone call to Perth cost which starts at 13:48 and finishes at 15:03?

8 $\boxed{} \times 17 = 27 \times 12 - 18$ What number belongs in the empty box?

9 A jar has a mass of 310 g when empty. When it is full of jam the total mass is 570 g. Tamsin has two jars of jam, one is half full and the other is three quarters full. What is the total mass of the two jars?

10 $8 \boxed{} 4 \boxed{} 3 \boxed{} 10 \boxed{} 5 = 18$ Copy out this calculation with $\div$ / $\times$ / $+$ / $-$ each used once only to give the correct answer.

11 A snail is at the bottom of a well which is 30 m deep. Each day it crawls up 3 metres but each night it drops down 2 metres. How many days does it take to reach the top of the well?

12 Ronnie sells wine. He is paid £200 per week plus one third of the value of the wine he sells. Last year he earned £22900. What was the value of the wine he sold?
(assume 1 year = 52 weeks)

UNIT 4

4.1 Constructing triangles

You must use a protractor and ruler to construct each diagram below.

1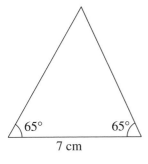

2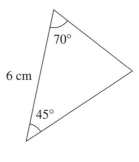

3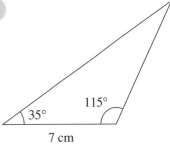

4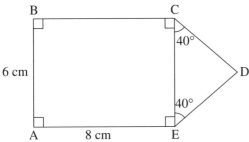

Measure the length AD.

5 Construct each triangle and measure the length AB each time.

a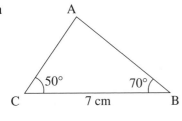

b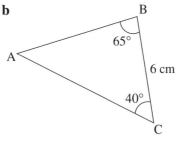

c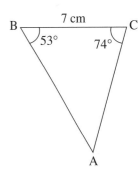

6 Construct the rhombus shown below.

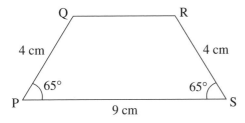

Measure PQ̂R.

7 Construct the kite shown below. AC = 5 cm.

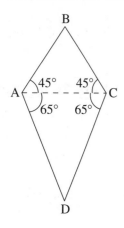

Measure the lengths of AB and AD.

HWK 2M/2E _____ **Main Book page 209**

1 Use a ruler and a pair of compasses to construct the triangles below. For each triangle, measure the angle x.

a
5.5 cm   4.8 cm
x
7 cm

b
6 cm   8.7 cm
x
6.9 cm

c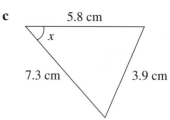
5.8 cm
x
7.3 cm   3.9 cm

2 Construct triangle PQR where PQ = 4.9 cm, QR = 6.6 cm and PR = 7.2 cm. Measure QP̂R.

3 Construct the shapes below. For each shape, measure the angle x.

a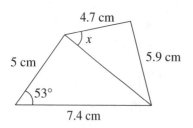
4.7 cm
x
5 cm   5.9 cm
53°
7.4 cm

b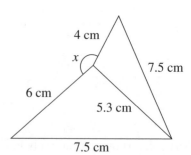
4 cm
x
6 cm   7.5 cm
5.3 cm
7.5 cm

4 Construct a quadrilateral PQRS where PQ = 4.8 cm, QR = 5.4 cm, RS = 6.8 cm, PS = 6.7 cm and QS = 7.3 cm (sketch the shape first if necessary). Measure PŜR.

4.2 Two dimensional shapes

HWK 1M ──────────────────────────── **Main Book page 212**

1 Which triangle below is equilateral?

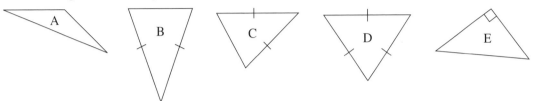

2 What is the name of a triangle with three different sides and three different angles?

3 Which quadrilateral below is a trapezium?

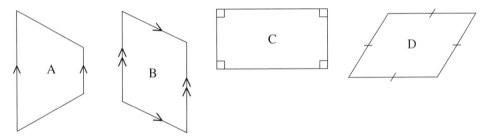

4 Draw a parallelogram (use a ruler!)

5 Name the shapes below which are hexagons.

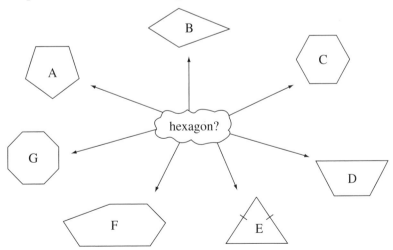

6 Draw any quadrilateral which has no parallel sides.

7 Write down the names of any quadrilaterals which have right angles inside them.

8 Draw a regular pentagon.

9 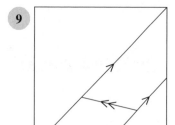 How many trapeziums can you see in this diagram?

| **HWK 1E** | **Main Book page 214** |

1 Draw a rhombus and show all its lines of symmetry.

2 What is the order of rotational symmetry of this parallelogram?

3 Which common quadrilaterals have one line of symmetry only?

4 What is the order of rotational symmetry of an isosceles triangle?

5 How many lines of symmetry does a parallelogram have?

6 How many lines of symmetry does this shape have?

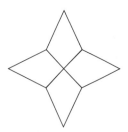

7 How many lines of symmetry does a regular octagon have?

8 Draw a quadilateral which has one line of symmetry only and no parallel sides.

9 Draw a quadrilateral which has one pair of parallel sides only but no lines of symmetry.

10 Name a common quadrilateral which has the same order of rotational symmetry as a trapezium.

4.3 Percentages

1 Change these percentages into decimals.

    a 49%   **b** 40%   **c** 8%   **d** 13%   **e** 85%

2 How much of this rectangle is shaded?   (45%) or (0.35)

3 Change these decimals into percentages.

    a 0.24   **b** 0.6   **c** 0.59   **d** 0.64   **e** 0.06

4 Holly owns 12 spanners. She uses 3 of these spanners when mending her bike. What percentage of the spanners did she use?

5 Which number is the larger? $\dfrac{2}{25}$ or (9%)

6 Which number is the larger? $\dfrac{13}{20}$ or (0.64)

7 Write the numbers below in order of size, smallest first

    a $\dfrac{3}{10}$, 0.4, $\dfrac{1}{4}$ **b** $\dfrac{2}{5}$, 38%, 0.39   **c** 0.7, $\dfrac{18}{25}$, 69%

8 There are five pairs of equivalent numbers below. Match each pair and write them down.

    | $\dfrac{4}{25}$ | 95% | 0.75 | 0.16 | 20% |

    | $\dfrac{19}{20}$ | 0.3 | $\dfrac{1}{5}$ | 30% | $\dfrac{3}{4}$ |

9 Change these percentages into fractions.

    a 37%   **b** 65%   **c** 14%   **d** 32%   **e** 22%

10 Answer True or False for each of the following statements.

    a $\dfrac{1}{3} = 0.03$ **b** $\dfrac{3}{25} = 12\%$ **c** $8\% = 0.8$

    d $0.18 = 18\%$ **e** $12\tfrac{1}{2}\% = \dfrac{1}{8}$ **f** $\dfrac{11}{20} = 55\%$

86

1. Terry has finished $\frac{2}{5}$ of his homework. What percentage of his homework does he still have to do?

2. What percentage of these shapes are stars?

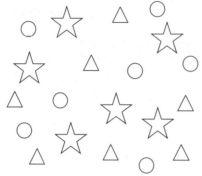

3. Donna has used up $66\frac{2}{3}\%$ of her petrol. What fraction of her petrol does she have left?

4. There are 6 weeks remaining until the summer holiday. What percentage of the school year is remaining if there are 40 weeks in the school year?

5. Harku needs to score 44% or more to pass a test. Does he pass the test if he scores 12 out of 25?

6. 760 out of 2000 people asked said they would go to the Olympics in 2012. What percentage of these people said they would *not* go?

7. Amelia spends her time working, playing sport, watching TV and playing music. What percentage of her time does she spend working?

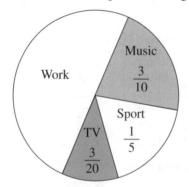

8. Find the largest number by writing these as percentages.

   $\left(\frac{63}{90}\right)$ $\left(\frac{12}{16}\right)$ $\left(\frac{18}{25}\right)$

9. 55% of the children at a large party were girls. If there were 36 boys at the party, how many girls were there?

You may use a calculator. Give all answers to the nearest percentage.

1 Hans is given £83. He spends £68. What percentage of the money has he still got?

2 There are 842 students in Elmwood High School. Last Monday 73 students were absent from school. What percentage of students came to school last Monday?

3 What percentage of the squares are filled with crosses?

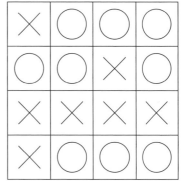

4 This chart shows the amount of fat, fibre and sugar in a 40 g serving of three different breakfast cereals.

a What percentage of 'Lush' is fibre?

b What percentage of 'Sunshine' is fat?

c What is the difference in the percentage of sugar in 'Lush' compared to 'Shake off'?

	Sunshine	Shake Off	Lush
fat	7.3 g	4.9 g	10.4 g
fibre	6.8 g	4.5 g	3.7 g
sugar	5.8 g	3.6 g	8.9 g

d What percentage of 'Sunshine' is *not* fat, fibre or sugar?

5 What percentage of these numbers are square numbers?

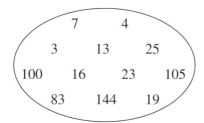

6 The pie chart shows the favourite subjects of some children in Elmwood High School.

a What percentage of the children chose maths?

b What percentage of the children chose history?

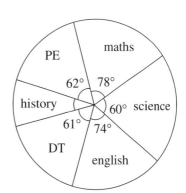

88

1 Work out

    a 80% of £50   **b** 5% of 60 kg   **c** 70% of £160

2 240 people are on a train. 40% of the people get off at Manchester and 15% get off at Birmingham. How many people are now on the train if nobody else gets on?

3 Work out the answers then put the questions in order of size, starting with the smallest.

    a 20% of £350   **b** 15% of £400   **c** 80% of £80

4 A worm measures 60 mm. Two months later it has grown by 40%. How long is the worm now?

5 Jackie weighs 70 kg. She follows a diet and loses 5% of her weight. How much does she weigh now?

6

Shirt	Shoes	Trousers	Coat
£40	£60	£45	£80
30% off	40% off	$33\frac{1}{3}$% off	55% off

Noel has £35 to spend in the sales. Which of the above items could he buy if he wanted to?

7 Josh earns £300 each week and is given a pay increase of 15%. Diane earns £340 each week and is given a pay increase of 5%. Who earns the most money now and by how much?

8 Work out

    a $17\frac{1}{2}$% of £3000   **b** $17\frac{1}{2}$% of £560   **c** $17\frac{1}{2}$% of £44

9 A sofa costs £1420 plus $17\frac{1}{2}$% VAT. What is the total price of the sofa?

10 Make up your own question which uses the numbers £80, 20% and the word 'decreases'.

Use a calculator when needed.

1   **a** Find 1% of 470   **b** Find 24% of 470

2 What is the difference between 12% of £49 and 14% of £47?

3   **a** Increase £6800 by 6%   **b** Decrease £560 by 8%
    c Reduce £730 by 14%   **d** Increase £310 by 43%

4 Jackie has a piece of wood 120 cm long. She cuts off 16% of the wood. How long is the piece of wood now?

5

A	B	C
Shirt	Shirt	Shirt
£38	£42	£37
9% off	12% off	6% off

a Which shirt is the cheapest to buy?

b Which shirt is the most expensive to buy?

c What is the difference between the cheapest and the most expensive price?

6 Work out to the nearest penny:

a 8% of £25.19   **b** 47% of £895.36

c Increase £154.23 by 13%   **d** Decrease £58.16 by $3\frac{1}{2}$%

7 Helen is 1.5m tall. How tall is she if she grows another 6%?

8 A coat costs £78.25. Its price is decreased by 14%. Two weeks later the new price is increased by 14%. How much does the coat now cost?

9 Ollie buys a 330 ml can of coke and drinks 58% of the coke. Marie then drinks 73% of the remaining coke. How much coke is left in the can? (give your answer to the nearest ml)

4.4 Proportion and ratio

HWK 1M/1E   **Main Book page 226**

1 Find the cost of 9 pens if 5 pens cost £6.50.

2 The total cost of 9 exercise books is £4.68. What is the total cost of 8 exercise books?

3 What proportion of this rectangle is shaded?

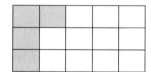

4 In a supermarket you can buy 4 toilet rolls for £1.68 or 6 toilet rolls for £2.58. Which is the cheaper price per toilet roll?

5 A 160g sausage roll contains 60g meat. What proportion of the sausage roll is meat?

6 A car travels 200 km in 120 minutes. How long will it take to travel 50km?

7 Some sweets cost 33p for 50g. How much would $\frac{1}{4}$ kg of the sweets cost?

8 A painter uses 108 pots of paint to finish painting 24 houses. How many pots of paint will he use to finish painting 72 houses?

9 The pie chart shows the favourite hot drink for the teachers in a school.

a What proportion prefer tea?

b What proportion prefer hot chocolate?

10 6 pickers collect 1500 apples in 5 hours. How many apples would 9 pickers collect in 7 hours?

11 11 dogs eat 22 tins of dog food in 6 days. How many tins of dog food would 8 dogs eat in 5 days?

12 Simone uses n gallons of petrol to travel 250 miles. How much petrol will Simone use to travel 400 miles?

13 x people take w hours to paint a house. How long would it take y people to paint the same house?

14 £30 can be exchanged for $54. How many dollars can be exchanged for £85?

HWK 2M ──────────────────────────────── **Main Book page 227**

1 There are 19 adults on a bus. 13 are female. Write down the ratio of females to males.

2 Write down the ratio of black circles to white circles.

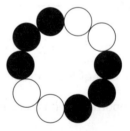

3 Copy this diagram. Colour in so that the ratio of black squares to white squares is 3:1.

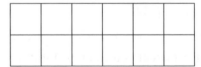

4 Write these ratios in simplified form.

a 2:16	**b** 8:24	**c** 20:15	**d** 42:28	**e** 85:35
f 32:56	**g** 12:24:30	**h** 27:18:63	**i** 36:60:84	

5 Peter has eleven 50 p coins and seven £1 coins. Write down the ratio of 50 p coins to £1 coins.

6 Complete the empty boxes to make the ratios *equivalent* to each other.

     a 25:15 = 5:☐   **b** 14:21 = ☐:3   **c** 40:5 = ☐:1

     d 70:90 = 7:☐   **e** 24:16 = ☐:2   **f** 27:36 = 3:☐

7 Consider the numbers from 1 to 20. Write down the ratio of how many prime numbers there are to how many non-prime numbers there are.

8 Write down the ratio of the number of months in the year containing the letter R to the number of months in the year which do not contain the letter R.

HWK 2E	Main Book page 229

1 Share £60 in the ratio   **a** 2:1   **b** 7:3   **c** 2:3

2 Mrs Dennis gives her two children £135 in the ratio 7:2. How much money is each share?

3 Sid and Aisha share chocolates in the ratio 3:4. If Sid gets 15 chocolates, how many chocolates does Aisha get?

4 The ratio of black sheep to white sheep in a field is 4:7. If the total number of sheep is 55, how many white sheep are there?

5 The ratio of boys to girls in a school assembly is 6:5. How many boys are there if there are 70 girls?

6 The tables below show how two sums of money were split.

£350
Alan : Max
5 : 2

£520
Donna : Hilary
1 : 3

How much more money does Donna get than Max?

7 Jane does a survey and finds that the ratio of blue cars to red cars to yellow cars is 6:1:5. If there are 36 cars, how many cars of each colour are there?

8 The ratio of men to women in a theatre are 5:2. What proportion of the people are women?

9 Dan, Josh and Elaine have 775 little toy soldiers between them in the ratio 7:9:15. How many soldiers does each child have?

10 Sue, Marvin and Lucy have £1180 in the bank shared between them in the ratio 16:23:20. Marvin takes out £100 and Lucy puts some more money into the bank. Their total money is now in the ratio 8:9:12. How much more money did Lucy put into the bank?

4.5 Negative Numbers

1 Work out

   a $-6 + 2$ **b** $-4 + 3$ **c** $4 - 7$ **d** $-5 + 3$ **e** $3 - 8$

   f $-2 - 1$ **g** $-4 - 3$ **h** $-6 + 4$

2 Which of these sums give the answer in the middle

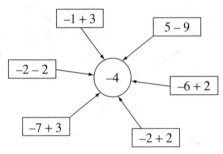

3 Work out

   a $5 - 2 - 6$ **b** $4 + 1 - 8$ **c** $-3 - 2 + 1$ **d** $-4 + 3 - 4$ **e** $6 - 4 - 4$

   f $-5 - 2 + 3$

4 Find the missing number?

$$-4 + 2 - 3 + ? = -1$$

5 Work out

   a $6 - (-4)$ **b** $5 + (-3)$ **c** $3 - (-9)$ **d** $-2 + (-3)$ **e** $-1 + (-5)$

   f $-2 - (-1)$ **g** $-6 - (-4)$ **h** $-5 + (-4)$

6 Write true or false for each statement below.

   a $7 + (-5) = -2$ **b** $-3 - (-4) = -7$ **c** $-4 - (-1) = -3$ **d** $-4 + (-3) = -7$

   e $5 - (-4) = 1$ **f** $2 + (-6) = -4$

7 Copy and complete this number square.

+	–4				
–2			–8		
		–1		–6	
			3	6	
	1				6
		–5			

8 Work out $-6 + (-3) - (-5) - 4 + (-2)$

Work out

1 **a** $7 \times (-4)$ **b** $3 \times (-2)$ **c** -3×6 **d** $-24 \div 3$

      e $-36 \div (-4)$ **f** -7×6 **g** $16 \div (-4)$ **h** $-50 \div (-10)$

2 **a** $20 \div (-5)$ **b** $30 \div (-6)$ **c** $-10 \div 2$ **d** -9×4

      e $8 \times (-5)$ **f** $-40 \div (-8)$ **g** -3×8 **h** $6 \times (-4)$

3 Copy this number chain and fill in the empty boxes

$$\boxed{6} \xrightarrow{\times} \boxed{-3} = \boxed{} \xrightarrow{\div} \boxed{2} = \boxed{} \xrightarrow{\div} \boxed{-3} = \boxed{} \xrightarrow{\times} \boxed{-7} = \boxed{}$$

4 Work out

      a $(-5)^2$ **b** $(-4) \times (-2) \times (-6)$ **c** $6 \times (-4) \times (-1)$

      d $(-4)^2$ **e** $(-3) \times 4 \times 7$ **f** $(-3)^3$

5 Copy this number chain and fill in the empty boxes.

$$\boxed{-2} \xrightarrow{\times} \boxed{-3} = \boxed{} \xrightarrow{\times} \boxed{-5} = \boxed{-30} \xrightarrow{\div} \boxed{} = \boxed{15} \xrightarrow{\div} \boxed{} = \boxed{-5}$$

6 Copy and complete this multiplication square.

×		−3	7		
		21			
−8					
5					
		18			30
9	−36			−18	

4.6 More algebra

1 Simplify the following expressions where possible.

      a $4x - 2x$ **b** $3y - y$ **c** $3y + 2$

      d $5x + 4 - x - 2$ **e** $7p + 3q - 2q + 5p$ **f** $9w + 6 + 3m - w$

2 $v = u + at$ Find the value of v when $u = 16$, $a = 10$ and $t = 3$.

94

3 Which expression is the odd one out?

$3n + 2 + n$ | $5n$ | $2n + 3 - 1 + 2n$

4 There are 36 people on a bus. At the cinema x people get off the bus and y people get on. Write down an expression for the number of people on the bus now.

5 $a = b^2 - c^2$ Find the value of a when $b = 9$ and $c = 4$.

6 $m = y(2y + 1)$ Find the value of m when $y = 6$.

7 Simplify

a $\frac{w}{w}$ **b** $y \times 9$ **c** $\frac{8m}{m}$ **d** $5x + 3 + \frac{x}{x}$

8 Henry has £m. Penny has £9 less than Henry. Donald has twice as much money as Penny. Write down an expression for the amount of money Donald has.

9 Simplify

a $3m \times 4n$ **b** $mn + nm$ **c** $5mn + 3m - nm$ **d** $6 \times 3mn$

10 $w = \frac{3(a - b)}{a}$ Find the value of w when $a = 6$ and $b = 2$.

HWK 1E   **Main Book page 236**

1 Simplify

a $3p \times q \times 6r$ **b** $4xy + 3x + 2xy - x$ **c** $6mn + 3nm + 6m + 3$

d $8xy \times 4 \times 6z$ **e** $8pq + 7 + 2qp - 9pq$ **f** $5a + 3a + 4ab$

2

Find an expression for the area of this trapezium. Simplify your answer as far as possible.

(trapezium: top $8ab$, left side $3c$, bottom $14ba$)

3 $y = 25 - x$
Find y when $x = -7$

4 $m = 16 + n$
Find m when $n = -7$

5 $a = 9b$
Find a when $b = -4$

6 $y = 6x + w$
Find y when $x = -4$ and $w = 8$

7 $p = 5q - n$
Find p when $q = -7$ and $n = -4$

8 $c = 3d + 7e$
Find c when $d = -5$ and $e = -3$

9 $m = 3(6 + n)$
Find m when $n = -8$

10 $a = b^2$
Find a when $b = -4$

11 $y = x(14 - p)$
Find y when $x = -3$ and $p = -8$

12 $m = nx - w$
Find m when $n = 3$, $x = -7$ and $w = -10$

13 $p = q^2 - r$
Find p when $q = -7$ and $r = -5$

14 $a = bc + d$
Find a when $b = 6$, $c = -9$ and $d = -3$

HWK 2M ———————————————————— **Main Book page 237**

Find the weight x by removing weights from both pans. Weights are in kg.

1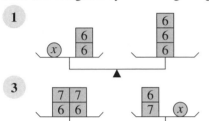

2

3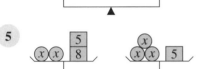

4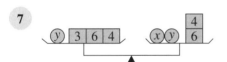

5

6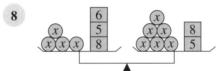

7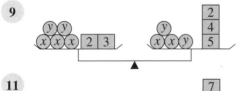

8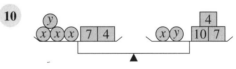

9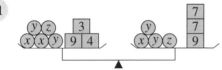

10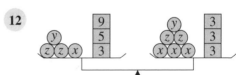

11

12

HWK 3M ———————————————————— **Main Book page 239**

Solve the equations below to find n.

1 $n - 5 = 6$

2 $n - 14 = 8$

3 $10 = n + 6$

4 $n - 10 = 12$

5 $3n = 18$

6 $24 = 3n$

7 $4n = 0$

8 $\dfrac{n}{4} = 9$

9 $\dfrac{n}{7} = 6$

10 $5n = 200$

11 $\dfrac{n}{8} = 6$

12 $12 = \dfrac{n}{3}$

Solve the equations below to find x.

13 $7x = 49$

14 $19 = x + 7$

15 $\dfrac{x}{6} = 8$

16 $x + 34 = 60$

17 $9x = 108$

18 $57 = 19x$

19 $32 = x - 17$

20 $15 = \dfrac{x}{3}$

21 $6x = 1$
$n = \dfrac{1}{6}$

22 $20 = \dfrac{x}{11}$

23 $173 = x - 258$

24 $\dfrac{x}{50} = 15$

HWK 3E ──────────────────────────────── **Main Book page 239**

Solve the equations below to find n.

1 $5 = \dfrac{n}{9}$

2 $2n = \dfrac{1}{4}$

3 $91 = 13n$

4 $\dfrac{n}{20} = \dfrac{1}{2}$

5 $374 = n - 247$

6 $n - \dfrac{1}{4} = \dfrac{3}{8}$

7 $30n = 0$

8 $\dfrac{1}{3}n = 42$

9 $17 = n + 17$

Solve the equations below to find x.

10 $\dfrac{x}{14} = 39$

11 $x + 0.17 = 4.6$

12 $x + \dfrac{1}{3} = \dfrac{5}{12}$

13 $x - 1.26 = 5.9$

14 $\dfrac{x}{100} = 0.4$

15 $15 = x + 3.7$

16 $x - \dfrac{3}{4} = \dfrac{1}{3}$

17 $\dfrac{1}{4}x = 3.2$

18 $x + \dfrac{1}{2} = 0.65$

19 $0.2 = x - \dfrac{3}{5}$

20 $0.03 + x = \dfrac{1}{20}$

21 $2.74 = \dfrac{x}{3}$

HWK 4M ──────────────────────────────── **Main Book page 240**

Solve the equations below to find x.

1 $4x + 1 = 13$

2 $5x - 4 = 31$

3 $8x - 7 = 1$

4 $7x + 8 = 71$

5 $9x - 14 = 22$

6 $10x - 70 = 130$

7 $5x = 3$

8 $5 = 8x - 11$

9 $4 = 7x$

10 $77 = 4x + 17$

11 $3x + 7 = 8$

12 $3x - 39 = 36$

Solve the equations below to find n.

13 $7n - 2 = 3$ **14** $9n + 13 = 85$ **15** $8n - 20 = 36$

16 $10 + 3n = 11$ **17** $9 = 6n + 9$ **18** $12 + 5n = 512$

19 $5n - 7 = 5$ **20** $77 = 2n + 17$ **21** $20n - 7 = 33$

22 $8 + 9n = 12$ **23** $3n - 4 = 1$ **24** $23 = 5n - 22$

HWK 4E   **Main Book page 241**

Solve the equations below to find x.

1 $29 = 4x + 1$ **2** $41 = 6x - 7$ **3** $15 = 8x - 9$

4 $62 = 7x - 8$ **5** $9 = 6x + 4$ **6** $11 = 30x - 6$

7 $64 = 13 + 3x$ **8** $5x + 17 = 17$ **9** $45 = 24 + 3x$

10 $12 = 14x + 9$ **11** $74 = 5x - 16$ **12** $31 = 20 + 6x$

Solve the equations below to find n.

13 $53 = 8n + 5$ **14** $16 = 2n + 5$ **15** $3n - 37 = 323$

16 $730 = 4n - 270$ **17** $17 + 3n = 25$ **18** $36 = 10n - 25$

19 $152 = 6n - 58$ **20** $79 = 47 + 4n$ **21** $7n + 90 = 1000$

22 $2n - \dfrac{1}{8} = \dfrac{1}{4}$ **23** $297 = 2n - 93$ **24** $2 = 3n + \dfrac{1}{2}$

HWK 5M   **Main Book page 241**

In each question I am thinking of a number. Write down an equation then solve it to find the number.

1   I treble the number and then add 17. The answer is 35.

2   I multiply the number by 6 and then add 5. The answer is 41.

3   I multiply the number by 7 and then subtract 13. The answer is 43.

4   I multiply the number by 5 and then subtract 16. The answer is 29.

5   I multiply the number by 7 and then add 4. The answer is 88.

6   I multiply the number by 10 and then subtract 2. The answer is 1.

7   I multiply the number by 8 and then subtract 4. The answer is 3.

98

8   I multiply the number by 20 and then add 48. The answer is 67. $20x + 48 = 67$

9   I multiply the number by 12 and then subtract 73. The answer is 83. $12x - 73 = 83$

10   I multiply the number by 15 and then add 16. The answer is 50. $15x + 16 = 50$

| HWK 5E | Main Book page 242 |

1   Linda has four times as much money as her brother. Linda spends £3 and now has £29 left. How much money does her brother have?

2
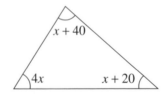

The perimeter of this rectangle is 48 cm. Write down an equation and then find the value of x.

3   Lesley has three times as many marbles as Mark but then Lesley loses 5 of her marbles. If Lesley now has 16 marbles, how many marbles does Mark have?

4   The length of a rectangle is 9 cm more than its width. If its perimeter is 42 cm, what is its width?

5   The sum of the ages of Karen, Mustafa and George is 62 years. Mustafa is three times as old as Karen and George is 7 years older than Karen. How old is Karen?

6   Write down an equation for the angles in this triangle then find the value of x.

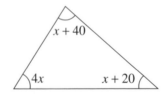

7   The length of a rectangle is 7 times its width. If the perimeter of the rectangle is 80 cm, what is its width?

8   An isosceles triangle has sides of length $(5x + 9)$, $(5x + 9)$ and 12 (all lengths are in cm). Find x if the perimeter of the triangle is 1 metre.

9   The sum of five consecutive numbers is 95. Find the five numbers.

10
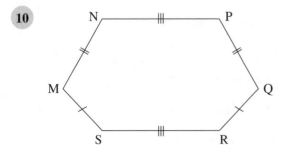

In this hexagon MN = PQ, MS = QR and NP = SR.
NP is three times MS.
PQ is 4 more than MS.
The perimeter of the hexagon is 128 cm.
Find the length of MS.

HWK 6M   **Main Book page 244**

Multiply out

1 $6(m + n)$ **2** $3(2x - 4)$ **3** $5(3p + 5)$

4 $8(4y - 5)$ **5** $6(2a + 3)$ **6** $2(x - y)$

7 $9(4 - q)$ **8** $3(2a + 5b)$ **9** $6(3m + 1)$

10 $7(3c + 2d)$ **11** $5(8w - 7)$ **12** $4(2a + b + 5)$

13 $9(2m - 9n)$ **14** $4(7p + 8q)$ **15** $3(8 + 3y - 7x)$

Expand

16 $c(d - 8)$ **17** $x(y + 3)$ **18** $a(a - 6)$

19 $p(3 + w)$ **20** $x(9 - x)$ **21** $4(3n + 2)$

22 $7(8a - 4)$ **23** $m(m - 2)$ **24** $5(3q - 9)$

25 $y(9 + y)$ **26** $b(4 - c)$ **27** $3(8w + 7)$

28 $4(3 + 6m)$ **29** $x(x - 4)$ **30** $a(7 - a)$

HWK 6E   **Main Book page 245**

Remove the brackets and simplify

1 $6(x + 4) + 3(x + 2)$ **2** $8(x + 5) + 5(x + 1)$ **3** $4(x + 7) + 2(x + 9)$

4 $3(2x + 3) + 6(x + 7)$ **5** $7(3x + 4) + 9(x + 2)$ **6** $8(2x + 4) + 3(x - 5)$

7 $5(4x + 2) + 2(x - 4)$ **8** $9(x + 6) + 3(2x - 7)$ **9** $8(6 + 2x) + 3(4x - 1)$

10 $4(9x + 3) - 17x$ **11** $12x + 5(3x + 6)$ **12** $7 + 4(6 + 4x)$

13 $25x + 4(2x + 5)$ **14** $9(3 + 4x) - 12$ **15** $6(5x + 2) + 2(3x - 5)$

16 $6(10x + 3) + 19x$ **17** $18 + 7(3 + 5x)$ **18** $7(6x + 1) + 4(2 - 3x)$

19   Which expression is the odd one out?

     a $\boxed{2(5x + 8) + 3(x - 5)}$ **b** $\boxed{4(x + 1) + 9x - 2}$ **c** $\boxed{3(2x + 5) + 7(x - 2)}$

UNIT 5

5.1 Rotation

Copy each diagram below and then draw its new position after it has been turned (you may use tracing paper).

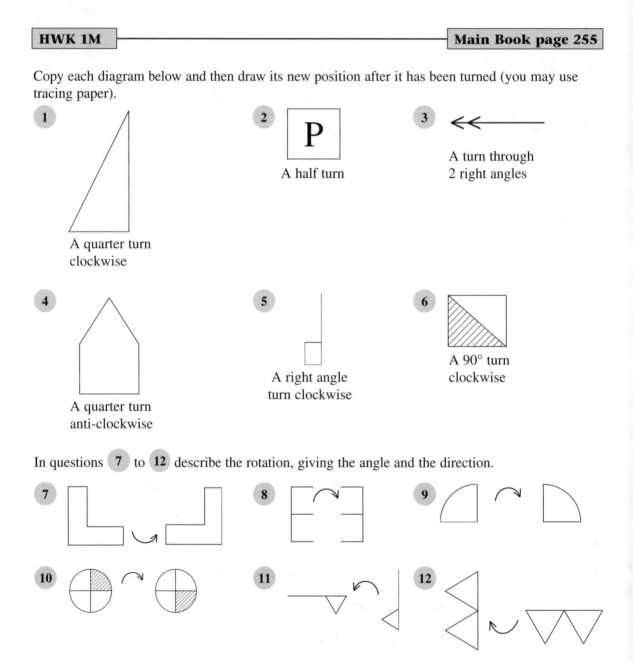

1

A quarter turn clockwise

2

P

A half turn

3

A turn through 2 right angles

4

A quarter turn anti-clockwise

5

A right angle turn clockwise

6

A 90° turn clockwise

In questions **7** to **12** describe the rotation, giving the angle and the direction.

7

8

9

10

11

12

1

a Copy this triangle on squared paper
b Draw the triangle after a quarter turn anti-clockwise around the point A.

2

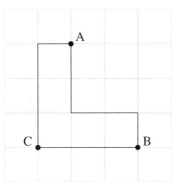

a Copy this shape on squared paper.
   Draw the image of the shape
b after a 90° rotation anti-clockwise about A
c after a half turn about B
d after a 90° rotation anti-clockwise about C.

3

a Copy this shape on squared paper.
   Draw the image of the shape
b after a 90° rotation clockwise about P
c after a 180° rotation about Q.

4 The diagram shows some shapes which have been rotated. Which shape do you get when you:

a rotate shape M 90° clockwise about A
b rotate shape R 90° clockwise about B
c rotate shape N 90° anti-clockwise about C
d rotate shape R 180° about D.

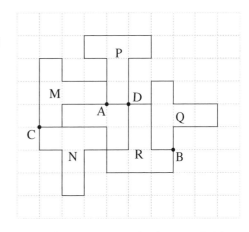

5

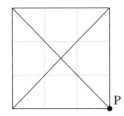

Draw this shape on squared paper. Draw the image of this shape after a 45° rotation anti-clockwise about P.

HWK 2M/2E ──────────────────────────────── **Main Book page 258**

 This shape fits onto itself six times when rotated through a complete turn. It has *rotational symmetry* of *order* six.

1 For each diagram decide whether or not the shape has *rotational symmetry*. If yes, write down the *order*.

a   **b**   **c**   **d**

e   **f**   **g**   **h**

2 Copy each diagram and complete it so that the final design has rotational symmetry of the order stated.

a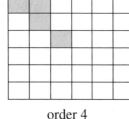

order 4

b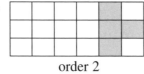

order 2

c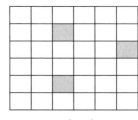

order 4

3 Find a picture of an object in a magazine or on the internet which has rotational symmetry. Bring the picture to your next maths lesson.

HWK 1M ──────────────────────────────── **Main Book page 260**

1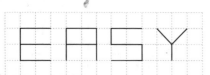

a Which of these letters has no line of symmetry?

b Which of these letters has rotational symmetry of order 2?

2 Which digit between 2 and 9 has rotational symmetry of order 2?

3 Copy the shapes below on squared paper and complete them with the lines of symmetry shown.

a 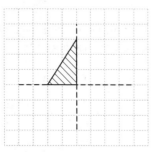   **b** 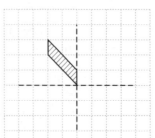   **c**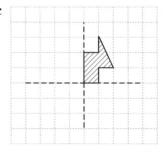

4 Draw a shape with line symmetry but no rotational symmetry.

5 **a** Does this shape have line symmetry?
If so, how many lines?

b Does this shape have rotational symmetry?
If so, what is the order?

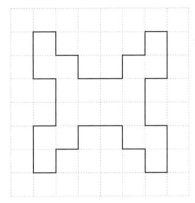

HWK 1E Main Book page 261

1

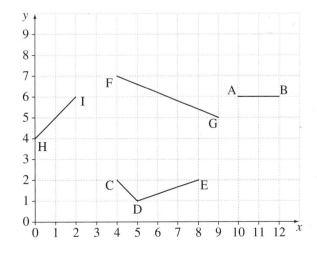

Write down the equations of all the lines of symmetry for:

a triangle A

b trapezium B

c rectangle C

d square D

2 **a** Copy this diagram

b AB is one side of a rectangle which has a line of symmetry $y = 4$. Draw the complete rectangle and write down the equation of the other line of symmetry

c Using CDE, complete the kite with a line of symmetry $y = 2$

d Using FG, complete the isosceles triangle with a line of symmetry $y = 7$

e Using HI, complete the square with lines of symmetry $y = 4$ and $x = 2$. Write down the equations of the other two lines of symmetry.

104

Copy each diagram and shade in as many squares as necessary so that the final pattern has mirror lines shown by the broken lines. For each question write down how many new squares were shaded in.

1
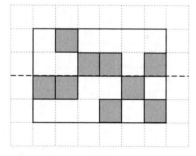

4
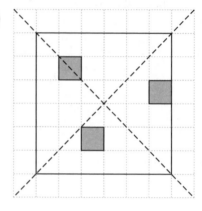

2
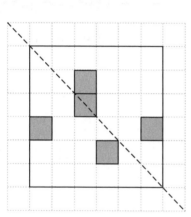

5
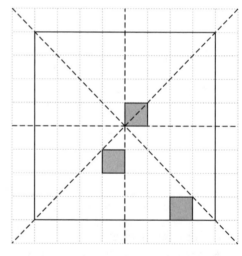

3
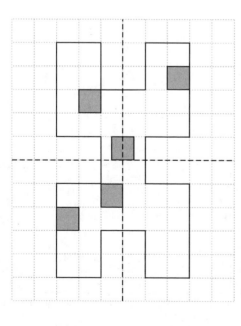

6

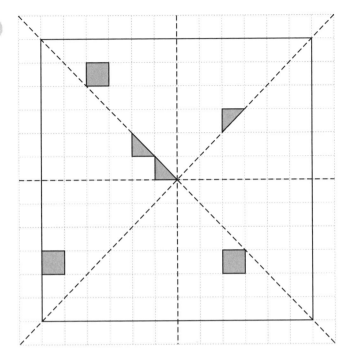

5.3 Translation

HWK 1M/1E   **Main Book page 266**

1   What shape do you move to when you:

    a translate shape Q 2 units right, 2 units down

    b translate shape S 2 units left, 3 units down

    c translate shape R 6 units left, 3 units down

    d translate shape Q 8 units right, 2 units down.

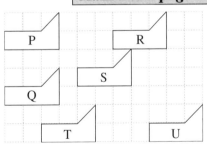

2 P_1 A_1 R_1 T_1

       T_2

         R_2

           A_2

             P_2

Describe the following translations.

    a A_1 A_2

    b R_1 R_2

    c T_1 T_2

    d P_2 P_1

106

3 Draw shape Y. Draw the image of Y after a translation of 1 unit to the right and 1 unit up.

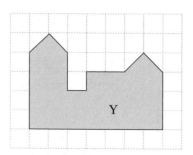

5.4 Number review

HWK 1M ──────────────────────── **Main Book page 269**

1 Copy and complete:

'All the factors of 30 are 1, 2, ☐, 5, ☐, ☐, ☐ and 30'

2
```
   16    64
  80   30   40
      56
```
a Which number is not a multiple of 8?

b Which number is a factor of 32?

3 Write down all the prime numbers between 10 and 20.

4 **a** Write down all the factors of 40.

b Write down all the factors of 50.

c Write down the Highest Common Factor of 40 and 50.

5 Write down the smallest prime number which is larger than 50.

6 Find three numbers that are multiples of both 4 and 7.

7 Find the LCM of 8 and 6. (LCM is the Lowest Common Multiple)

8 Find the Highest Common Factor (HCF) of

a 15 and 35   **b** 12 and 20   **c** 36 and 54

9 By finding all the factors, explain why 4 is different to 2, 3 and 5.

HWK 2M ──────────────────────── **Main Book page 271**

1 Change these fractions into percentages.

a $\dfrac{7}{100}$ **b** $\dfrac{8}{25}$ **c** $\dfrac{3}{5}$ **d** $\dfrac{32}{200}$ **e** $\dfrac{19}{20}$

2 Change these decimals into fractions (cancel down when possible).

a 0.6   **b** 0.19   **c** 0.35   **d** 0.32   **e** 0.02

3 Which number is the odd one out? $\dfrac{3}{30}$ 0.303   0.1

4 Cancel down each fraction to its lowest terms.

a $\dfrac{10}{25}$ b $\dfrac{14}{20}$ c $\dfrac{4}{16}$ d $\dfrac{15}{18}$ e $\dfrac{9}{24}$ f $\dfrac{12}{30}$

5 Work out

a $\dfrac{5}{8}-\dfrac{1}{4}$ b $\dfrac{1}{2}+\dfrac{1}{3}$ c $\dfrac{4}{5}-\dfrac{1}{2}$ d $\dfrac{1}{6}+\dfrac{1}{3}$ e $\dfrac{7}{8}-\dfrac{1}{2}$

f $\dfrac{2}{3}-\dfrac{1}{4}$ g $\dfrac{3}{8}+\dfrac{1}{3}$ h $\dfrac{1}{4}+\dfrac{3}{5}$

6 Write the following in order of size, smallest first,

a $0.42, \dfrac{2}{5}, 45\%$ b $\dfrac{1}{20}, 0.2, 10\%$ c $\dfrac{7}{10}, 73\%, 0.68$

7 Ryan scored $\dfrac{12}{25}$ in a French test. The pass mark is 45%. Did Ryan pass the test?
If so, by how much?

8 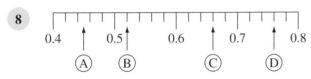 Write down which letter on the scale belongs to each number below?

HWK 3M Main Book page 272

Work out

1 14×24 **2** $864 \div 36$ **3** $1353 \div 41$ **4** 117×27

5 461 eggs are packed into 38 boxes of 12 eggs. How many eggs are left over?

6 14 people pay £266 for a meal. How much does each person pay if they each pay an equal amount.

7 Copy and complete

a $\square \div 39 = 12$ b $837 \div \square = 31$ c $\square \times 48 = 1536$

8 36 Easter eggs are packed into each box. A supermarket orders 17 boxes. The supermarket sells 557 eggs. How many Easter eggs does the supermarket still have?

9 Which is larger and by how much?

$752 \div 47$ or $364 \div 28$

108

1 Work out

    a $7.3 + 11.5$ **b** $5 + 9.6$ **c** $3 - 0.17$ **d** $43.6 - 16$

    e 6.12×6 **f** $7.8 \div 5$ **g** 3×2.59 **h** $0.62 + 3 + 0.1$

    i $34.4 \div 8$ **j** $16 - 7.4$ **k** $30.1 \div 7$ **l** 8×2.37

2 Jean weighs 59.2 kg at the start of the week. At the end of the week she weighs 58.83 kg. How much weight has she lost?

3 Copy and complete

    a
$$
\begin{array}{r}
3 \cdot 6 \ \Box \\
+ \ \Box \cdot \Box \ 3 \\
\hline
7 \cdot 3 \ 8
\end{array}
$$

    b
$$
\begin{array}{r}
2 \cdot 9 \ \Box \\
+ \ 5 \cdot \Box \ 8 \\
\hline
\Box \cdot 3 \ 4
\end{array}
$$

    c
$$
\begin{array}{r}
8 \cdot \Box \ 7 \\
- \ \Box \cdot 6 \ \Box \\
\hline
5 \cdot 4 \ 3
\end{array}
$$

4 Five books cost £28. How much does each book cost?

5 A rubber weighs 8.6g. How much do 7 rubbers weigh?

6 Copy and complete the number chain.

7 Work out

    a 0.462×100 **b** 0.8×0.03 **c** $23 \div 1000$ **d** 0.006×0.7

    e 1.6×0.3 **f** 3.7×0.16

8 Hannah and two friends buy a tent for £43.95. Hannah pays one third of the cost of the tent and also buys a sleeping bag for £23.48. How much change will Hannah get from two £20 notes?

1 Work out

    a 30% of £80   **b** 4% of 300 kg   **c** $\frac{3}{5}$ of 20 cm   **d** $\frac{3}{8}$ of 56 m

    e 35% of 60 g   **f** $\frac{9}{10}$ of 80 km   **g** 25% of £1068   **h** $\frac{7}{9}$ of 63 cm

2 Which is larger?    or $\left(\frac{1}{3} \text{ of £21} \right)$

3 Copy and complete

    a $\Box$% of 900 = 180   **b** $\frac{2}{3}$ of $\Box$ = 12   **c** 5% of $\Box$ = 6

4 Use a calculator to work out

    a 9% of £420   **b** 17% of 2400 g   **c** 30% of £316

5 16% of the crowd of 41500 people watching Chelsea play Liverpool are Liverpool fans. How many Liverpool fans were at the match?

6 Copy and complete

    a $\frac{3}{50} = \square$ %   **b** $\frac{2}{3} = \square$ %   **c** $\frac{3}{4} = \square$ %   **d** $\frac{11}{20} = \square$ %

7 Which answer is the odd one out?

    | 12% of £4900 | $\frac{1}{3}$ of £1773 | $\frac{4}{5}$ of £735 |

8 Work out (69% of £8300) − ($\frac{3}{7}$ of £10801)

9 Work out 9% of 7% of £2900

10 Which is larger and by how much?

    Increase £326 by 17.5%   or   Decrease £613 by two–fifths

5.5 Probability 2

HWK 1M/1E   **Main Book page 275**

1 A bag contains 2 red balls and 3 blue balls. It I take out one ball, what is the probability that it will be:

    a a blue ball

    b a red ball?

2 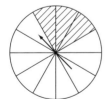 What is the probability of spinning a shaded part on this spinner?

3 Each of the first seven prime numbers is written on a separate card. One of these prime numbers is chosen at random. What is the probability of choosing

    a a number less than 6

    b a single digit number

    c an even number

4 There are 18 socks in a drawer. 8 are blue, 7 are grey and the rest are red. Jan selects a sock at random. What is the probability that she selects:

  a a grey sock   **b** a red sock   **c** a green sock   **d** a blue or a grey sock

  e a blue, grey or red sock

5 One of these cards is selected at random.
What is the probability of selecting:

  a the letter R

  b a ?

  c a vowel

H   A   R   D

E

R

?

6 A fair dice is rolled. Are you more likely to get an odd number or a number greater than 4? *Explain* your answer.

7 | 1 | 3 | 4 | 4 | 7 | 9 | 9 | 9 | 10 | 11 |

A card is selected at random. Find the probability of selecting

  a a number greater than 9   **b** an even number

  c a prime number   **d** a square number

  e A card numbered 9 is added to the cards above. What is now the probability of selecting a prime number?

HWK 2M   **Main Book page 278**

1 Sally needs to throw a '6' with a fair dice to start a game. What is the probability that she will *not* get a '6' with her next throw?

2 Den has 7 goldfish and 3 pink fish in a tank.

  a He selects a fish at random to give to his nephew. What is the probability that he selects a goldfish?

  b After giving one goldfish to his nephew, he buys four more pink fish. If he now selects one fish at random, which type of fish is he most likely to pick? *Explain* your answer.

3 One card is picked at random from a pack of 52. Find the probability that it is

  a the Ace of hearts   **b** a King   **c** a red card   **d** a diamond

4 A ball is selected at random from this bag.
Find the probability that it is

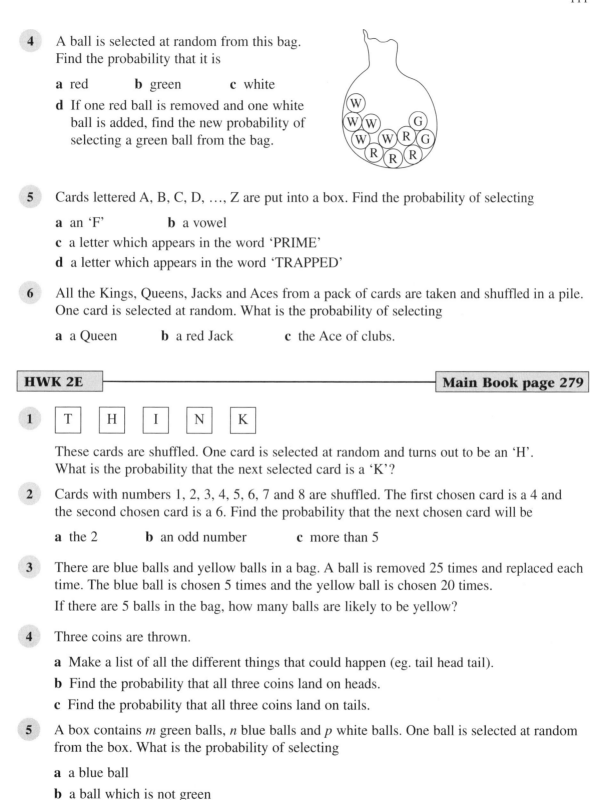

a red   **b** green   **c** white

d If one red ball is removed and one white
ball is added, find the new probability of
selecting a green ball from the bag.

5 Cards lettered A, B, C, D, …, Z are put into a box. Find the probability of selecting

a an 'F'   **b** a vowel

c a letter which appears in the word 'PRIME'

d a letter which appears in the word 'TRAPPED'

6 All the Kings, Queens, Jacks and Aces from a pack of cards are taken and shuffled in a pile.
One card is selected at random. What is the probability of selecting

a a Queen   **b** a red Jack   **c** the Ace of clubs.

HWK 2E   **Main Book page 279**

1   T   H   I   N   K

These cards are shuffled. One card is selected at random and turns out to be an 'H'.
What is the probability that the next selected card is a 'K'?

2 Cards with numbers 1, 2, 3, 4, 5, 6, 7 and 8 are shuffled. The first chosen card is a 4 and
the second chosen card is a 6. Find the probability that the next chosen card will be

a the 2   **b** an odd number   **c** more than 5

3 There are blue balls and yellow balls in a bag. A ball is removed 25 times and replaced each
time. The blue ball is chosen 5 times and the yellow ball is chosen 20 times.

If there are 5 balls in the bag, how many balls are likely to be yellow?

4 Three coins are thrown.

a Make a list of all the different things that could happen (eg. tail head tail).

b Find the probability that all three coins land on heads.

c Find the probability that all three coins land on tails.

5 A box contains m green balls, n blue balls and p white balls. One ball is selected at random
from the box. What is the probability of selecting

a a blue ball

b a ball which is not green

6

pattern 1   pattern 2   pattern 3

Black and white tiles are used to make the patterns shown above.

a One tile is selected at random from pattern 4. What is the probability that it is black?

b One tile is selected at random from pattern 5. What is the probability that it is white?

7 There are x dogs and y cats in kennels. One morning an alsatian dog arrives and two siamese cats leave. What is the probability that the next animal to leave will be a dog?

5.6 Interpreting graphs

HWK 1M/1E ──────────────────────── **Main Book page 283**

1 This graph shows the number of people in a supermarket one day.

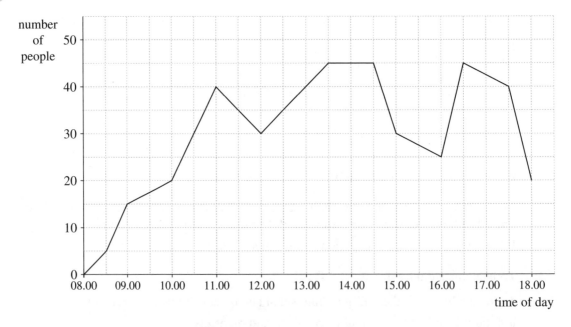

a How many people were in the supermarket at

(i) 12.00   (ii) 10.30   (iii) 08.30

b At what time were 15 people in the supermarket?

c At what two times were there 20 people in the supermarket?

d How long did it take in the afternoon for the number of people to increase from 25 to 45?

2

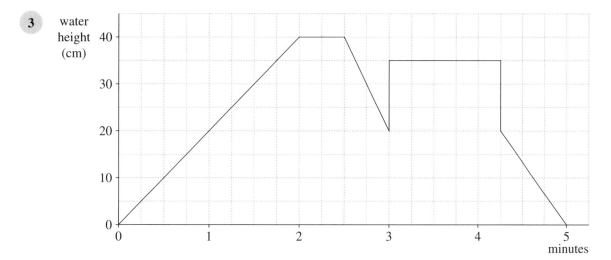

The graph above converts cm into inches.

a Convert into inches

   (i) 10 cm   (ii) 20 cm   (iii) 5 cm

b Which is longer? 15 cm or 7 inches

3

Meg runs a bath then gives her baby a quick bath. The graph above shows the water height during 5 minutes.

a What was the water height after 30 seconds?

b What was the water height after 1 minute 45 seconds?

c When did the baby go into the bath?

d How long was the baby in the bath for?

e What probably happened after $2\frac{1}{2}$ minutes?

f How long did the bath take to empty once the baby had been taken out of the bath?

114

1

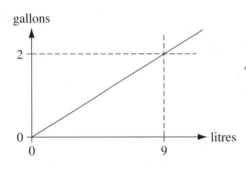

gallons / litres graph

Draw a graph to convert litres into gallons. Draw a line through the point where 9 litres is equivalent to 2 gallons.

Use a scale of 1 cm to 1 litre across the page and 2 cm to 1 gallon up the page.

Use your graph to convert

a 0.6 gallons into litres

b 6.3 litres into gallons

2 Rob burns off 9 kcals for every one minute on an exercise bike.

a Draw a graph to show what Rob burns off during 10 minutes on the exercise bike.

b Use your graph to find out how long it takes Rob to burn off 31.5 Kcals.

c Use your graph to find out how many Kcals have been used after 7 minutes 30 seconds.

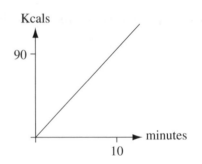

1 The graph shows a car journey from Manchester.

a How far is it from Leeds to Sheffield?

b For how long does the car stop in Leeds?

c How much further is it to Leeds at 09.30?

d What is the speed of the car from Manchester to Leeds?

e How long does the car take to get from Leeds to Sheffield after it stopped?

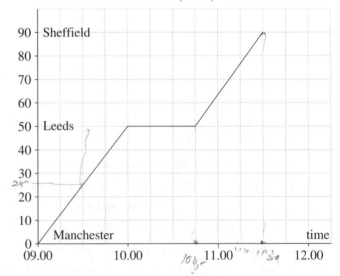

45 mph

2

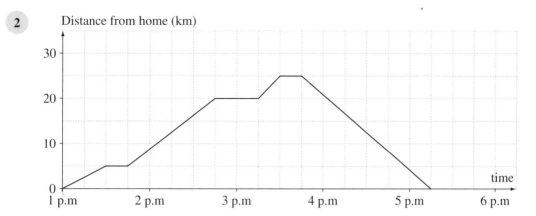

Distance from home (km)

Callum goes for a bike ride. The graph shows how far he was from his home.

a How long did he stop for at 2.45 p.m.?

b At what time did he set off for home?

c How many times did he stop on his journey?

d What was his speed on his journey between his first stop and his second stop?

3 **a** Draw a travel graph on squared paper to show Roger's journey below. (Use a horizontal axis from 09.00 to 12.00 and a vertical axis from 0 to 10)

Roger leaves home at 09.00 and cycles 9 miles in 45 minutes. He then stops for half an hour before cycling towards home. After cycling 3 miles in a quarter of an hour, he has a puncture and stops for 30 minutes to mend it. He then cycles home at a steady speed of 8 miles per hour.

b At what time did Roger arrive home?

c What was Roger's speed during the first 45 minutes of his journey?

4 Pam leaves home at 08.00 and walks for 1 hour 15 minutes at a speed of 4 miles per hour (mph). She stops at the post office for a quarter of an hour then walks for another 30 minutes at 2 mph. She stops in a supermarket for half an hour then starts walking home at a speed of 2 mph. After 30 minutes she increases her speed to 5 mph. She returns home at this speed.

Her partner also leaves home at 08.00 and walks at a steady speed of 2 mph until he reaches the supermarket.

a Draw a graph to show these journeys.

b At what time do Pam and her partner meet during the journey?

c At what time does Pam arrive home?

5.7 Rounding numbers

HWK 1M **Main Book page 292**

1 Round off each number to the accuracy shown.

    a 1763 (nearest 100)   **b** 275 (nearest 10)   **c** 92450 (nearest 1000)

    d 316500 (nearest 1000)   **e** 2550 (nearest 100)   **f** 17.5 (nearest whole number)

2 Answer true or false.

    a 650 → 700 (to nearest 100)

    b 4.5 → 5 (to nearest whole number)

    c 17500 → 17000 (to nearest 1000)

    d 465 → 470 (to nearest 10)

3 Work out the following using a calculator and then round the answer to the *nearest ten.*

    a 13.6×19.4 **b** 6.3×274 **c** $3186 \div 48.9$

    d $197.3 + 258.6$ **e** $\sqrt{4980}$ **f** $5948.7 - 3176.8$

4 Which of these numbers round off to the nearest hundred shown in the middle?

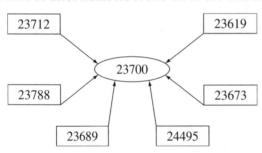

5 Work out the following using a calculator and then round the answer to the *nearest whole number.*

    a 7.13×4.9 **b** $17.6 - 9.18$ **c** 18.7×3.24 **d** $39.4 \div 13$

    e 18.23×4.7 **f** $5.216 + 19.9$ **g** $158.6 \div 9.7$ **h** $\sqrt{28}$

HWK 1E **Main Book page 293**

1 Round these numbers to one decimal place.

    a 3.82   **b** 7.91   **c** 23.45   **d** 3.718

    e 8.649   **f** 8.0231   **g** 38.693   **h** 24.2684

    i 4.325   **j** 2.5813

2 Write the following numbers correct to 2 decimal places.

a 5.6837 **b** 24.7168 **c** 0.49468 **d** 0.08712

e 104.8652 **f** 9.0594 **g** 13.06283 **h** 427.60843

3 Which of these numbers round off to the one decimal place number shown in the middle?

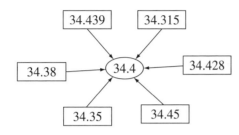

4

a Write down the length and width in cm, correct to one decimal place.

b Use a calculator to work out the area of the rectangle, giving your answer to one decimal place.

5 Work out these answers on a calculator and then write the answers correct to one decimal place.

a 3.2 × 7.3 **b** 12 ÷ 9 **c** 9.14 ÷ 8.7 **d** 4.106 + 3.689

e 0.4 ÷ 0.092 **f** $\sqrt{3.8}$ **g** 5.3 − 1.938 **h** 29.2 × 13.67

6 Use a calculator and this time write the answer correct to 2 decimal places.

a 19 ÷ 7 **b** 5.81 × 6.93 **c** $\sqrt{7} \times \sqrt{6}$ **d** 38 ÷ $\sqrt{67}$

118

$201.6 \times 3.9 \approx 200 \times 4 \approx 800$

Decide, by estimating, which of the three answers for each calculation below is closest to the exact answer.

	Calculation	A	B	C
1	19.8×101.2	2000	3000	1000
2	2.03×39.7	100	60	80
3	$405 - 199.83$	150	300	200
4	$3008 \div 201.4$	15	150	60
5	$503 \div 20.3$	250	25	5
6	1.99×61.2	120	60	12
7	1503×9.91	15000	3000	1000
8	$0.312 + 0.673$	0.1	1	5
9	7.19×16.03	10	200	110
10	19% of £598	£12	£60	£120
11	4.1×789314	32 million	3.2 million	320 000
12	11% of £398.13	£30	£4000	£40
13	$\sqrt{63.75}$	6	8	12
14	8.23×5.08	40	13	400
15	19.88^2	400	200	40

1   A box of chocolates costs £5.95.
     Estimate the cost of 30 boxes of chocolates.

2   Estimate the area of this triangle.

3   Dani earns £793.25 each month.
     Estimate how much she earns in one year.

4   A pen costs £3.05.

     a Estimate the cost of 15 pens.
     b Find the exact cost of 15 pens.

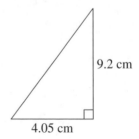

9.2 cm

4.05 cm

5

pineapple	£1.96
washing powder	£4.05
tin of beans	£0.49

Dean buys 3 pineapples, 2 boxes of washing powder and 5 tins of beans. Estimate the total cost.

6 Use estimation to decide which calculation below gives the largest answer.

7.03×29.6 12.1×19.78 $1587 \div 8.14$

7 The area of a rectangle is 2406.5 cm². If its length is 59.92 cm, estimate its width.

8 Tallulah pays £71.50 each month into a savings plan. She does this for 10 years. Estimate the total amount she pays into the plan.

9 Joey is paid £11964 each year. Estimate how much money he has left each week if he has to pay £81 rent each week.

10 Write down each calculation and insert the correct answer from the list given. Use estimation.

a $4076.4 \div 79$ **b** $\sqrt{80.2816}$ **c** 3.91×6.04

d 29% of 2016   **e** 8.2×1.9 **f** $14.749 \div 0.49$

Answers: 8.96   15.58   30.1   23.6164   584.64   51.6

5.8 Circles

HWK 1M/1E ———————————————— **Main Book page 297**

Remember : Circumference = π × diameter

1   5 cm
a Write down the radius of this circle.
b Write down the diameter of this circle.
c Calculate the circumference (to one decimal place).

2   18 cm
a Write down the radius of this circle.
b Write down the diameter of this circle.
c Calculate the circumference (to one decimal place).

3 For each circle, calculate the circumference correct to one decimal place.

a 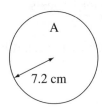 14 cm

b 8 m

c 3 cm

d 38 mm

4 A coin has a diameter of 17.5 mm. Work out its circumference, correct to one decimal place.

5 A circular lake has a radius of 150 m. Carys runs three times around the outside of the lake. How far does she run in total? (give your answer to the nearest metre)

6

A 7.2 cm

Which circle has the larger circumference and by how much? (give your answer to one decimal place)

B 15.3 cm

HWK 2M **Main Book page 301**

Remember : area = πr²

1 Calculate the area of each circle and give your answers to one decimal place.

a 9 cm

b 13 m

c 46 mm

d 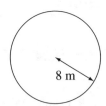 8 m

2 A circular road sign has a radius of 32 cm. Calculate the area of the road sign, correct to one decimal place.

3 A circle of diameter 7 m is painted onto a sports pitch. Calculate the area of grass within the circle, correct to one decimal place.

4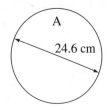

A 24.6 cm

Which circle has the larger area and by how much? (give your answer to one decimal place)

B 11.9 cm

HWK 2E ——————————————————— | **Main Book page 302**

1 Calculate the area of each shape and give your answers to one decimal place.

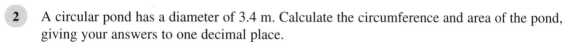

a 13 m b 22 cm c 4 m d 15 cm

e 2.5 m f 19 cm g 6.4 m h 10 cm 60° 10 cm

2 A circular pond has a diameter of 3.4 m. Calculate the circumference and area of the pond, giving your answers to one decimal place.

3 A bicycle wheel has a diameter of 82 cm. How far does the bike travel when the wheel turns round ten complete circles (ie. ten complete revolutions). Give your answer to the nearest cm.

4

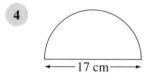

17 cm

A dressmaker cuts out a semi-circular piece of fabric of diameter 17 cm.

a What is the area of this piece of fabric? (to one decimal place)

b What is the perimeter of this piece of fabric? (to one decimal place)

UNIT 6

6.1 More equations

1 Solve these equations:

     a $4y = 48$ **b** $x - 9 = 12$ **c** $\frac{n}{4} = 8$

     d $\frac{m}{5} = 15$ **e** $8p = 1$ **f** $\frac{a}{9} = 7$

2 Solve

     a $3p - 8 = 1$ **b** $12y - 38 = 82$ **c** $5x + 17 = 37$

     d $3m + 2 = 3$ **e** $6n - 2 = 3$ **f** $7w + 12 = 75$

3 Sarah thinks of a number, multiplies it by 6 and subtracts 18. The answer is 48. Write down an equation then solve it to find Sarah's number.

4 Solve these equations:

     a $7n - 3 = 3$ **b** $10 = 4x + 9$ **c** $16 + 5p = 20$

     d $2 = 8y - 3$ **e** $14 = 13 + 7w$ **f** $6 = 15m - 7$

5 Frances buys 6 pencils and spends 80p on a drink. She spends £2.42 in total. How much did each pencil cost?

6 Solve

     a $\frac{1}{6}m = 13$ **b** $3p + \frac{1}{4} = 1$ **c** $8n = \frac{1}{3}$

1 Solve these equations:

     a $4(n + 3) = 24$ **b** $8(w - 5) = 16$ **c** $3(3y + 1) = 57$

     d $5(2x - 1) = 85$ **e** $7(2m + 3) = 91$ **f** $2(2p - 6) = 36$

2 Cho thinks of a fraction, multiplies it by 8 then adds 9. The answer is 12. Write down an equation then solve it to find Cho's fraction.

3 Solve

     a $10w - 3 = 3$ **b** $30x - 9 = 11$ **c** $3 = 6y - 5$

4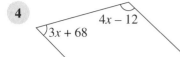

Write down an equation involving x then solve it to find the value of each angle.

5 Solve these equations:

a $7 = 9w + 2$ **b** $4(2n - 3) = 44$ **c** $5y - 6 = 8$

d $8(2p + 1) = 16$ **e** $51 = 3(2 + 5m)$ **f** $7 + 15x = 10$

6

6 cm

(3x + 4) cm

The area of this rectangle is 96 cm².

a Write down an equation involving x then solve it to find x.

b What is the perimeter of this rectangle?

6.2 Sequence rules

HWK 1M   **Main Book page 315**

1 Here is a sequence of shapes made from sticks.

shape number n: 1   2   3

number of sticks s: 5   9   13

a Draw shape number 4 and count the number of sticks.

b Write down the rule for the number of sticks in a shape.
'The number of sticks is____ times the shape number and then add____'.

c Write the rule connecting n and s without using words, ie. write '$s = $ .....'

2 These dots make a sequence.

Shape number 1

Shape number 2

Shape number 3

a Draw shape number 4.

b Make a table:

shape number n	1	2	3	4
number of dots d	8	12	16	

c Write down the rule. 'The number of dots is____ times the shape number and then add____'.

d Write the rule connecting n and d without using words, ie. write 'd = ...'

3 Here is another sequence of shapes made from sticks.

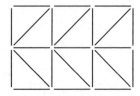

Shape number 1   Shape number 2   Shape number 3

a Draw shape number 4.

b Make a table:

shape number n	1	2	3	4
number of sticks s				

c Write down the rule.
'The number of sticks is____ times the shape number and then add____.'

d Write the rule connecting n and s without using words, ie. write 's =.....'

HWK 2M ———————————————————————— **Main Book page 317**

1 The nth term of a sequence is $3n + 7$. What is the value of:

a the first term ($n = 1$)   **b** the fourth term ($n = 4$)

c the fiftieth term ($n = 50$)   **d** the thousandth term ($n = 1000$)

2 Write down the first 5 terms of a sequence if the nth term = $4n - 2$.

3 Which formula below for the nth term gives the sequence 3, 5, 7, 9,....?

| $3n$ | | $4n - 1$ | | $2n + 1$ | | $n + 2$ |

4 Write down the first 5 terms of a sequence if the nth term = $6n + 1$.

5 Which formula below for the nth term gives the sequence 7, 11, 15, 19, ...?

| $n + 4$ | | $7n$ | | $7n + 4$ | | $4n + 3$ |

6 Write down the coordinates of the bottom vertex (corner) of squares 1, 2 and 3.
The pattern continues. Find the coordinates of:

a the bottom vertex of square 4

b the bottom vertex of square 20

c the right-hand vertex of square 50

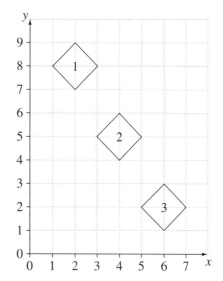

7 Match up each sequence and the correct formula for the nth term from the list given.

a 6, 11, 16, 21, ...   **b** 7, 14, 21, 28, ...   **c** 1, 4, 9, 16, ...   **d** 1, 4, 7, 10, ...

| $7n$ | $3n - 2$ | $n + 5$ | n^2 | $5n + 1$ |

8 Find the nth term formula for each sequence below:

a 3, 6, 9, 12, ...   **b** 5, 7, 9, 11, ...   **c** 5, 8, 11, 14, ...   **d** 5, 14, 23, 32, ...

6.3 Metric and imperial units

HWK 1M ———————————————————————— **Main Book page 322**

Remember: 1 kg = 1000 g,   1 litre = 1000 ml,   1 tonne = 1000 kg

1 Copy and complete each statement below.

a 3.5 m =   cm   **b** 60 mm =   cm   **c** 2.6 km =   m   **d** 200 g =   kg

e 7.5 litres =   ml   **f** 30 cm =   m   **g** 9.4 tonnes =   kg   **h** 4.6 cm =   mm

i 8500 g =   kg   **j** 8700 ml =   litres   **k** 0.4 kg =   g   **l** 350 m =   km

m 2.9 m =   mm   **n** 6.09 kg =   g   **o** 5.8 g =   mg   **p** 450 mm =   m

2 Fiona drank 357ml of water from a 1.5 litre bottle. How much water is left in the bottle?

3 Terry has walked 9.2 km in a 10 km race. How many metres has he still got to walk?

4 How many complete 170 ml drinks can be taken from a 2 litre bottle?

5 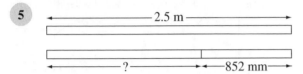 852 mm is cut off a 2.5 m piece of wood. How long is the remaining piece of wood?

HWK 1E ———————————————————— **Main Book page 322**

> Reminder:
>
> 1 foot = 12 inches   1 pound = 16 ounces   1 gallon = 8 pints
>
> 1 yard = 3 feet   1 stone = 14 pounds
>
> 1 mile = 1760 yards   1 ton = 2240 pounds

Copy and complete

1 9 yards =   feet

2 6 pounds =   ounces

3 72 inches =   feet

4 $\frac{1}{2}$ mile =   yards

5 $3\frac{1}{2}$ gallons =   pints

6 2 feet 6 inches =   inches

7 9 stones 7 pounds =   pounds

8 5 feet 3 inches =   inches

9 2.1 tons =   pounds

10 60 pints =   gallons

11 $7\frac{1}{4}$ pounds =   ounces

12 8 stones 13 pounds =   pounds

13 $2\frac{3}{4}$ gallons =   pints

14 2 yards 2 feet 9 inches =   inches

15 Jack weighs 9 stones. How much does he weigh if he loses 7 pounds?

16 Find the perimeter of this shape.

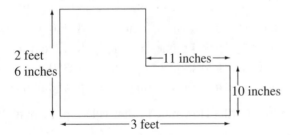

17 Rory has to pull out of a 3 mile race with 800 yards still to go. How many yards had Rory ran up to that point?

18 Rob weighs 13 stones 5 pounds then loses 9 pounds. Mary weighs 11 stones 13 pounds then puts on 10 pounds. Who now weighs the most and by how much?

HWK 2M ──────────────────────────── **Main Book page 323**

Reminder: 1 foot ≈ 30 cm   1 kg ≈ 2.2 pounds

            8 km ≈ 5 miles   1 gallon ≈ 4.5 litres

1 Copy and complete each statement below:

a 10 kg ≈   pounds   **b** 90 litres ≈   gallons   **c** 30 miles ≈   km

d 6.6 pounds ≈   kg   **e** 6 gallons ≈   litres   **f** 8 feet ≈   cm

g 44 pounds ≈   kg   **h** 32 km ≈   miles   **i** 6 kg ≈   pounds

2 The distance from Bristol to London is about 160 km. How many miles is this?

3 Tania is 5 feet tall. Mary is 1.48 m tall. Who is taller and by how much?

4 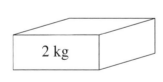  The box and the bag both contain sugar. Which contains the most sugar and by how much?

2 kg

4.5 pounds

5 Jim has 3 gallons of water in a water butt in his garden. How many litres will he have left if he uses 12 litres?

6 Put these amounts in order starting with the smallest. 1 foot, 40 cm, 8 inches, 0.43 m, 12 cm

7 Charlie wants 1.1 pounds of cheese. In a shop, how many grams of cheese must he ask for?

8 At a charity cake sale all the proceeds were collected in 10p coins and then the coins were arranged in a long straight line for a newspaper photo.
If the diameter of a 10p coin is just under one inch and the line of coins was 50 metres long, roughly how much money was raised?

128

1 Find the perimeter of the shape below in mm.

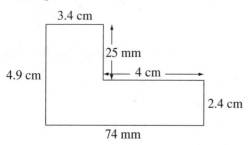

3.4 cm

25 mm

4.9 cm

4 cm

2.4 cm

74 mm

2 Find the perimeter of the shape below in cm.

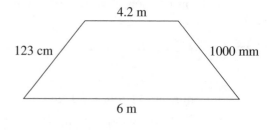

4.2 m

123 cm

1000 mm

6 m

3 A metal bar weighing 12.35 kg is melted down and made into metal balls each weighing 130 g. How many metal balls can be made?

4 A plant grows at a constant rate of 16.56 cm per day. How much, in mm, does it grow in one minute?

5 Calculate the area of each shape in cm².

a

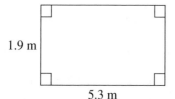

1.9 m

5.3 m

b

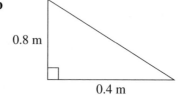

0.8 m

0.4 m

c

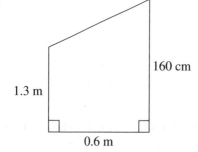

160 cm

1.3 m

0.6 m

6 A lorry arrives at a building site with 450 kg of waste already in it. A dumper truck empties 20 loads into the lorry. The lorry leaves with 2.93 tonnes of waste in it. On average, how heavy was the load emptied into the lorry each time?

7 A cafe usually serves 200 drinks of coke each day. Each drink is 275 ml. The cafe always allows for up to 20% extra to be sold on any one day. How many litres of coke must the cafe have in stock at the start of any day?

8 In the U.K. about 80000 tonnes of tobacco are smoked as cigarettes each year.

a If one cigarette weighs 0.8 g, work out how many cigarettes are smoked in the U.K. every year.
b If a packet of 20 cigarettes costs £4.50, how much is spent in the U.K. on cigarettes every year?

6.4 Angles and constructions

Find the angles marked with letters.

1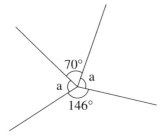

70°
a
a
146°

2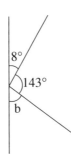

8°
143°
b

3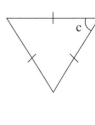

c

4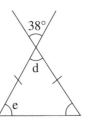

38°
d
e

5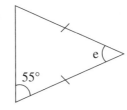

e
55°

6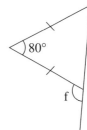

80°
f

7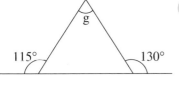

g
115°   130°

8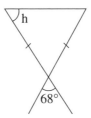

h
68°

9 Use a *protractor* to draw the following angles accurately.

  a 75°   **b** 43°   **c** 130°   **d** 115°   **e** 34°   **f** 230°

10 For each angle in question **9**, write down if it is acute, obtuse or reflex.

11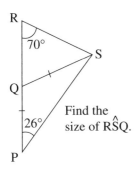

R
70°
S
Q
26°
P
Find the size of RŜQ.

12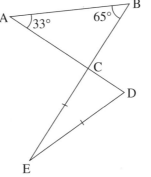

A 33°   65° B
C
D
E
Find the size of CÊD.

HWK 1E   **Main Book page 329**

Find the angles marked with letters.

1
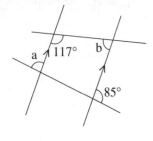

2
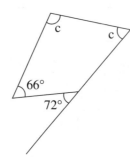

3
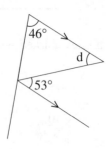

4
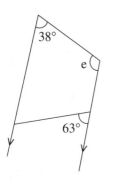

5
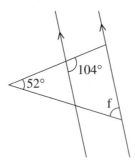

6
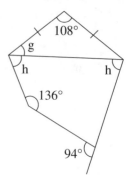

7
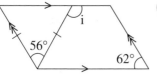

8
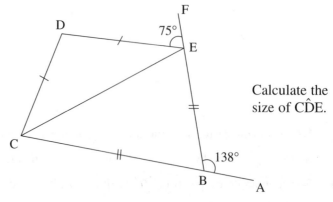

Calculate the size of CD̂E.

Find the value of x then calculate the size of QŜT.

HWK 2M ──────────────────────────────── **Main Book page 331**

1   Draw any 3 straight lines. Use a ruler and compasses to construct the perpendicular bisector of each line.

2   **a** Draw this rectangle accurately.

   b Construct the perpendicular bisector of PQ.

   c Construct the perpendicular bisector of NP.

   d Label the point of intersection Y as shown. Measure MY.

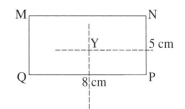

3   **a** Construct a triangle DEF with DE = 6 cm, EF = 4 cm and DF = 8 cm.

   b Construct the perpendicular bisector of the line DF and mark the point P where the bisector meets the line DE.

   c Measure DP.

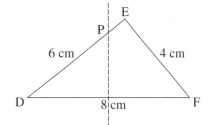

HWK 3M ──────────────────────────────── **Main Book page 333**

1   Use a protractor to draw an angle of 70°. Use a ruler and compasses to construct the bisector of the angle. Use a protractor to measure the angles to check that you have drawn the angle bisector accurately.

2   Draw an angle of 80°. Construct the bisector of the angle.

3   Draw an angle of 110°. Construct the bisector of the angle.

4   **a** Construct triangle PQR with PQ = 5.5 cm, QR = 8.2 cm and PR = 6.5 cm

   b Construct the bisector of the angle QP̂R and mark the point Y where the bisector cuts the line QR.

   c Measure PY.

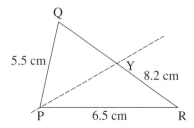

5   **a** Construct the equilateral triangle with each side 6 cm long.

   b Construct the bisector of angle BÂC.

   c Construct the bisector of angle AĈB.

   d Mark the point X where the two bisectors meet. Measure AX.

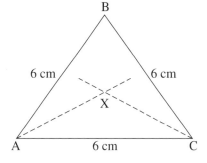

132

6.5 Three dimensional objects

1 Name these solids.

a   b 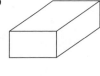 c 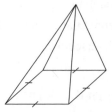 d

2 How many faces, vertices and edges has the object got in question **1** **c**?

3 Draw a triangular prism. How many vertices does a triangular prism have?

4 How many faces does a cube have?

5 What is the name of this object?

View from above   View from the side

6    **a** Draw a hexagonal prism.

   b How many faces, vertices and edges does a hexagonal prism have?

hexagon

7 The top of this pyramid (shaded part) is cut off. Look at the remaining bottom part. How many faces, vertices and edges does this part have?

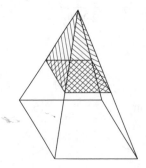

1   Draw an accurate net for this cuboid.

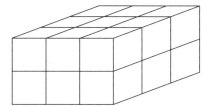

2   Name the object which can be made from this net.

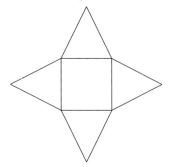

3   Draw a net for a closed cuboid measuring 4 cm by 2 cm by 1 cm.

4   Draw an accurate net for this triangular prism.

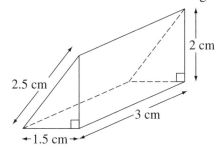

5   When the cuboid is made from this net, which face will be directly opposite the ▲?

	2		
1	▲	3	4
		5	

6   Sketch a possible net for a tetrahedron (triangular pyramid).

7 This is the net of a cuboid. The volume of this cuboid is 162 cm³. Find the missing length shown by the '?'

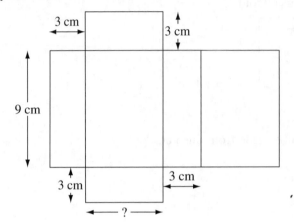